THE BOOK OF
FACTS

ADDITION

A Comprehensive Guide for Teaching
Addition Facts

JAMES BURNETT
CALVIN IRONS
ALLAN TURTON

ORIGO
EDUCATION

The Book of Facts: Addition

Copyright 2007 ORIGO Education
Authors: James Burnett, Calvin Irons, and Allan Turton

Burnett, James.
The book of facts: addition.

ISBN 978 1 921023 43 9.
ISBN 1 921023 43 0.

1. Addition - Study and teaching. 2. Addition - Problems,
exercises, etc. I. Irons, Calvin J. II. Turton, Allan. III. Title.

512.92

For more information visit www.origoeducation.com.

ISBN: 978 1 921023 43 9

10 9 8 7 6 5 4 3

Printed and Bound in Malaysia for Imago

Contents

Introduction

Introduction

BASIC FACTS

It is essential that all students are able to successfully calculate both mentally and with paper and pencil. The first significant step for calculating involves learning the basic number facts associated with each operation. The term *basic facts* refers to those facts that most people are expected to know automatically. The basic addition facts (and related subtraction facts) range from $0 + 0 = 0$ to $9 + 9 = 18$ inclusive. The basic multiplication facts (and related division facts) range from $0 \times 0 = 0$ to $9 \times 9 = 81$ inclusive. These facts form the basis for all future number work.

Research shows that the most effective way for students to learn the basic facts is to arrange the facts into *clusters*. Each cluster is based on a *thinking strategy* that students can use to help them learn all of the facts in that cluster (Fuson, 2003; Thornton, 1990). For example, *use doubles* is one of the addition clusters. Within that cluster are double facts and facts that involve doubling then adding 1 or 2.

In addition to teaching thinking strategies, a modern mathematics curriculum should include many opportunities for students to use and expand their thinking skills. Discussing the understandings students have about numbers and encouraging them to think about numbers and use operations in new ways, promotes *number sense*. This type of thinking is an excellent foundation for all computation and encourages creative and flexible thinking that is compatible with mental computation.

About this Series

Each title in *The Book of Facts* series is designed to help teachers develop their students' abilities to automatically and accurately recall the basic facts for each operation. Although the clusters of facts are individually addressed, they form part of a teaching sequence. The thinking involved in learning one set of facts is a prerequisite to learning the next set.

Each cluster of facts begins with a brief background on the strategy along with some preparation activities. Each cluster is then broken down further according to the sub-strategies used (see the contents page of each book). Activities in each strategy and sub-strategy are sequenced according to the following four stages of teaching and learning:

INTRODUCE

Hands-on materials, stories, discussions, and familiar visual aids are used to introduce the strategy or sub-strategy.

REINFORCE

These activities make links between concrete and symbolic representations of the facts being examined. Students also reflect on how the strategy or sub-strategy works and the numbers to which it applies.

PRACTICE

Games, worksheets, and other activities provide students with opportunities to apply and demonstrate their knowledge of the facts. At this stage, the students should use mental computation only and fast recall is stressed.

EXTEND

Students are encouraged to apply the strategy to numbers beyond the range of the basic number facts. The activities in this section are designed to further strengthen the students' number sense, or "feel" for numbers.

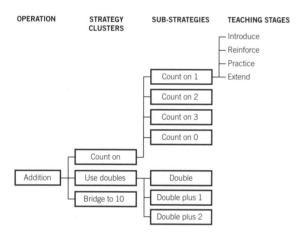

OPERATION	STRATEGY CLUSTERS	SUB-STRATEGIES	TEACHING STAGES

This diagram shows the general structure for *The Book of Facts: Addition*. Each book in the series covers one operation and involves grouping the facts into clusters around a thinking strategy and its sub-strategies.

Each book in *The Book of Facts* series contains fully reproducible blackline masters. Some pages feature *Fact Files* that provide definitions and interesting facts relevant to the activities on the page. The series also complements the resources included in *The Box of Facts*. Many of the resources referenced in *The Book of Facts: Addition* and *The Book of Facts: Subtraction* are included in *The Box of Facts: Addition/Subtraction*. Illustrated references to these resources are made in relevant activities. These references enable quick identification for teachers who have the resources and provide blueprints for teachers who prefer to make their own.

About this Book

In *The Book of Facts: Addition*, the strategies for the clusters of facts are *count on*, *use doubles*, and *bridge to 10*. Similar clusters are used for subtraction. The activities used in the first cluster also introduce the term *turnaround* to refer to those facts that reverse the order of the parts to be added. For example, $6 + 2 = 8$ is the same as $2 + 6 = 8$ because they both have a total of 8.

The *count-on* strategy involves counting (not necessarily by ones) to add 1, 2, 3, or 0 to a given number. All sixty-four of the addition count-on facts including their turnarounds are shown in yellow below.

+	0	1	2	3	4	5	6	7	8	9
0	0	1	2	3	4	5	6	7	8	9
1	1	2	3	4	5	6	7	8	9	10
2	2	3	4	5	6	7	8	9	10	11
3	3	4	5	6	7	8	9	10	11	12
4	4	5	6	7	8	9	10	11	12	13
5	5	6	7	8	9	10	11	12	13	14
6	6	7	8	9	10	11	12	13	14	15
7	7	8	9	10	11	12	13	14	15	16
8	8	9	10	11	12	13	14	15	16	17
9	9	10	11	12	13	14	15	16	17	18

The yellow shading in this table shows the count-on facts.

The *use-doubles* strategy involves doubling and doubling then adding 1 or 2. This strategy covers forty-four number facts, which include turnarounds.

+	0	1	2	3	4	5	6	7	8	9
0	0	1	2	3	4	5	6	7	8	9
1	1	2	3	4	5	6	7	8	9	10
2	2	3	4	5	6	7	8	9	10	11
3	3	4	5	6	7	8	9	10	11	12
4	4	5	6	7	8	9	10	11	12	13
5	5	6	7	8	9	10	11	12	13	14
6	6	7	8	9	10	11	12	13	14	15
7	7	8	9	10	11	12	13	14	15	16
8	8	9	10	11	12	13	14	15	16	17
9	9	10	11	12	13	14	15	16	17	18

The yellow shading in this table shows the use-doubles facts.

+	0	1	2	3	4	5	6	7	8	9
0	0	1	2	3	4	5	6	7	8	9
1	1	2	3	4	5	6	7	8	9	10
2	2	3	4	5	6	7	8	9	10	11
3	3	4	5	6	7	8	9	10	11	12
4	4	5	6	7	8	9	10	11	12	13
5	5	6	7	8	9	10	11	12	13	14
6	6	7	8	9	10	11	12	13	14	15
7	7	8	9	10	11	12	13	14	15	16
8	8	9	10	11	12	13	14	15	16	17
9	9	10	11	12	13	14	15	16	17	18

The yellow shading in this table shows the bridge-to-10 facts.

The table on page 2 and the table above show that some basic facts are covered by both strategies. For example:

6 + 2 = 8 is only a count-on fact.
3 + 2 = 5 is a count-on and a use-doubles fact.
5 + 6 = 11 is only a use-doubles fact.

The third strategy is called *bridge-to-10*. As the name suggests, the idea is to start with one number, bridge the gap to 10 by using part of the second number, then add the balance. Many of these facts are already covered by one of the first two strategies. There are thirty-three bridge-to-10 facts in total, which are shaded in the following table.

Fact File

The use-doubles strategy is also known as *near doubles*.

The bridge-to-10 strategy is also known as *bridge the decades*, *bridging across 10*, *bridging through 10*, *making 10*, *make to 10*, and *use 10*.

When covering the basic facts the focus should be on mastering the facts, not matching facts to strategies. The strategies help break the total number of facts into manageable parts and provide a means for the students to recall the facts quickly and accurately. However, if a student is able to figure out a fact with speed and precision using a different strategy than the one suggested, then the goal has been accomplished.

Assessment

In *The Book of Facts: Addition*, several blackline masters can assist in keeping track of how students progress in mastering the basic facts. Blackline Masters 14 and 25 provide a formal means of assessment. The sheets fold into quarters so that the students can see only one set of facts at a time. A reminder to use these sheets is given at the end of each *Practice* teaching and learning stage.

The following blackline masters can also be used to assess the facts covered in these sub-strategies (or strategy in the case of bridge to 10):

Count on 1:	Blackline Master 6
Count on 2:	Blackline Master 15
Count on 3:	Blackline Master 16
Count on 0:	Blackline Master 19
Double:	Blackline Master 22
Double plus 1:	Blackline Master 26
Double plus 2:	Blackline Master 28
Bridge to 10:	Blackline Master 30

The grid on Blackline Master 1 can be used to record student progress. The numerals in the first column on the left indicate the first addend of an addition fact. The numerals along the top row indicate the second addend. Where the row and column of these two numerals intercept is the total. A variety of markings, such as a simple ✓ or ✗, can be used to record whether or not a student can recall the fact both quickly and accurately. The Student Tracking Chart on Blackline Master 2 can then be used to record overall achievement for each student in the class.

The students will appreciate seeing the progress they make in covering the basic facts. Make an overhead transparency of Blackline Master 1 and as the class completes each strategy or sub-strategy, shade the relevant facts.

+	0	1	2	3	4	5	6	7	8	9
0	0	1	2	3	4	5	6	7	8	9
1	1	2	3	4	5	6	7	8	9	10
2	2	3	4	5	6	7	8	9	10	11
3	3	4	5	6	7	8	9	10	11	12
4	4	5	6	7	8	9	10	11	12	13
5	5	6	7	8	9	10	11	12	13	14
6	6	7	8	9	10	11	12	13	14	15
7	7	8	9	10	11	12	13	14	15	16
8	8	9	10	11	12	13	14	15	16	17
9	9	10	11	12	13	14	15	16	17	18

To use the grid to find the total of 5 + 2, locate the 5 in the first column on the left and the 2 in the top row. Where the row and column of these intersect is the total (7).

References

Fuson, K. C. (2003). Developing mathematical power in whole number operations. In J. Kilpatrick, W. G. Martin, & D. Schifter (Eds.), *A research companion to principles and standards for school mathematics* (pp. 68–94). Reston, VA: National Council of Teachers of Mathematics.

Thornton, C. (1990). Strategies for the basic facts. In J. N. Payne (Ed.), *Mathematics for the young child* (pp. 131–151). Reston, VA: National Council of Teachers of Mathematics.

Count On

Fact File

In the operation of addition, the parts that are being joined together are called *addends*. The total that they form is called the *sum*.

Turnarounds are an application of the commutative property of addition. This property allows any number of addends to be combined in any order and the sum will always be the same.

Counting is a vital life skill and forms the basis of the count-on strategy, which gives more than half the number of basic facts that need to be mastered. The count-on strategy involves counting on 1, 2, 3, or 0 from a greater, starting number. Examples include:

$$3 + 1 = 4 \qquad 7 + 2 = 9$$
$$8 + 3 = 11 \qquad 5 + 0 = 5$$

This section addresses the count-on-1 strategy first. Once this strategy is established, the idea of turnarounds is introduced to show the students that order is not important in addition. Using turnarounds allows students to see that $1 + 8 = 9$ is the same as $8 + 1 = 9$. Since it is easier to start with the greater number and count on 1, using turnarounds helps make simple addition much faster.

The sequence for teaching the count-on addition facts then continues with the count-on-2 facts and their turnarounds, the count-on-3 facts and their turnarounds, and then finally the count-on-0 facts and their turnarounds.

Prepare

1 Use Blackline Masters 3, 4, and 5 to make three sets of cards. Use each set separately. Mix up the cards and select one at random. Show the card for approximately three seconds and ask the students to tell you how many dots are on the card. Do this for each set of cards then mix the sets together and repeat the activity. Ensure that the students are competent in completing this activity before continuing any further.

2 Place ten counters in a container. Ask a student to randomly select some of the counters to place on the overhead projector. Encourage a volunteer to suggest a way to count the counters. They should move the counters as they count the number. For example:

"Seven is

two...   four...   six...   seven."

○○   ○○   ○○   ○

Encourage other members of the group to count the same number of counters in other ways and to move the counters as they count. For example:

"Seven is

one... two... three... four... five... six... seven."

○   ○   ○   ○   ○   ○   ○

"Seven is

two... four... five... six... seven."

○○ ○○ ○ ○ ○

As the students become more confident, ask them to say the greatest number they can see in the group (without counting). Instruct them to say the number and then count on from it to figure out the total number in the group. For example:

"Seven is

five...   six...   seven."

○○○○○   ○   ○

If the students point to the counters as they explain their thinking, encourage them to put one hand over the greatest number they see and to count the remainder of the group.

3 Ask the students to count forward from any number less than 10. Write a number on the board and select a student to count from this number to 12. Repeat the activity (using the same starting number) with other students in the group, then repeat the activity using another starting number. As the students become more confident, the count can be extended to 15 or 20.

4 Involve the students in quick counting activities. Explain that you are going to turn on the overhead projector for a short time and they will need to count the number of counters they can see. Demonstrate by turning the projector on for approximately three seconds and then turning it off again.

Fact File

The ability to identify a quantity of items without counting is called *subitizing*. Using counters that are identical will help reduce any distractions when subitizing.

With the projector turned off, arrange counters
on the screen as shown below.

Turn the projector on for two seconds and
then turn it off. Explain that you will show the
counters again for the same amount of time.
After the second showing, ask the students to say
the number of counters they think were on the
overhead projector. Turn on the projector and ask
individual students to explain how they counted.

Repeat the activity using a different number
of counters. Each time, arrange the counters so
that one or two counters are placed to the side
of the main group. For example, to show eight,
use arrangements like those shown below.

During the discussions, encourage the students to
count the number in the large group and then add
on the one or two counters at the side. Repeat this
activity several times.

5 ▷ Check that the students know that addition means
joining two or more parts to make one total group.
Encourage the students to use concrete materials
or pictures to help them describe what the
concept means.

Count On 1

Introduce

1 ▶ Collect nine bottles or other identical objects. Arrange three bottles in a row and ask the students to count as you position each bottle. Ask, How many bottles do I have? Place another bottle with the others and ask, How many bottles do I have now? Ask volunteers to describe how they knew what the new total was. For example they may say, "When I count, the next number after three is four. So three and one more is four."

2 ▶ Put five cubes into a container (e.g. a disposable cup). Write the number of cubes on the container. Hold another cube above the container so the students can see it and then drop it in, as shown in the diagram below. Ask, How many cubes are in the cup now? How do you know? Repeat this activity for any starting number up to 9.

3 ▶ Share some simple addition stories with the students. For example, Three birds are sitting on a fence. One more sits beside them. How many birds are on the fence now? Invite volunteers to provide their own stories for different count-on-1 facts. Some students may like to draw a picture and explain what it shows, or write their story.

4 ▶ Select or make the count-on-1 cards shown below.

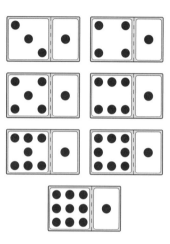

See: *Count-on Strategy Cards*

Choose a card and fold back the flap with one dot so the students cannot see it (see the diagram below). Ask them to tell you how many dots they can see without counting. Then fold the flap forward and ask the students to tell you how many dots there are in total. Repeat this activity several times with different cards. Make sure the cards are held so that the one dot to be added is on the right-hand side as seen from the front. In this way the students see and say the greater starting number first, then count on the lesser number as it is revealed.

"I see five and one more makes six.
Five add one is six."

Reinforce

1 Select or make laminated, blank count-on cards. Using a non-permanent marker, create count-on-1 cards that use digits instead of dots for the starting number. Repeat *Introduce* Activity 4 (page 8) using these cards. Afterward, give each student a copy of Blackline Master 6. Instruct them to draw one dot on each card and write the new numbers.

2 Have the students create their own number track as shown below. Say an expression such as 6 + 1. Ask the students to cover the correct answer on their track with a counter. Say more examples until they have covered each number on their track.

1	2	3	4	5	6	7	8	9	10

Say, **Look at seven. What numbers are on either side of seven?** (Six and eight.) **Which number do you finish on if you count on one from seven?** (Eight.) **What number do you start on if you count on one and finish at six?** (Five.) Repeat for other numbers on the track.

3 Show the students how to create a cube train using connecting cubes to show the number fact 6 + 1 = 7, as shown below. Instruct the students to each create a cube train that shows a count-on-1 fact with a total between 2 and 10. After the trains are made, invite individuals to identify their fact. Ask the students to raise their hands if they made the same fact.

4 Copy Blackline Master 7 and cut out the numeral cards. Select or make the count-on-1 cards shown. Display one of the count-on cards (do not use the 9 + 1 = ___ card) and invite a volunteer to select the matching numeral card. Repeat with other students and different count-on cards. Afterward, choose numeral cards and ask the students to identify the count-on-1 card that matches. The 9 + 1 = ___ card will be used in a later activity.

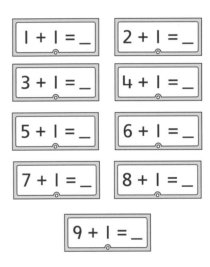

See: *Addition Flash Cards*

5 Using the cards from the previous activity, show the 5 + 1 = ___ flash card and the 8 numeral card beside it. Ask, **Does this make sense? Why not?** Encourage the students to explain their thinking. Repeat with other pairs of matching and non-matching cards.

$$5 + 1 = \underline{\quad} \qquad 8$$

Practice

1. Give each pair of students a copy of Blackline Master 8 and a paper clip. Direct the students to cut out one of the spinners and straighten part of the paper clip as shown below. Each student should then spin their paper clip and note the numeral that the tip eventually rests on. If the paper clip lands on 0 have them select another number. Instruct them to then count on 1 to figure out the total and to write the matching number fact. Repeat as time allows.

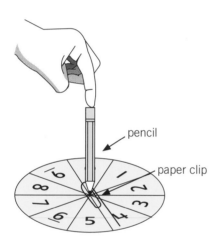

pencil

paper clip

2. Reuse the count-on-1 flash cards from *Reinforce* Activity 4 on page 9. Display one card and select a student to say the answer. Allow a few seconds for the student to provide the answer (under three seconds is a quick response). Repeat several times. Do not laminate the cards, as the turnarounds will be written on the back in a later activity.

3. Give each student a copy of Blackline Master 9 and twenty counters. Call out random count-on-1 expressions and ask the students to place a counter on each correct answer. When a student has four adjacent counters in a vertical, diagonal, or horizontal line they call out "Bingo" to win the game. The count-on expressions should range from $1 + 1$ to $9 + 1$.

2	7	2	6	8
5	3	8	3	7
9	6	4	9	4
8	10	7	5	10
5	4	9	8	6

When a student has four adjacent counters in a vertical, diagonal, or horizontal line they call out "Bingo" to win the game.

4. Give each student a copy of Blackline Master 10 and twenty counters. Repeat the previous activity by calling out numbers from 2 to 10. This time the students place a counter on the matching count-on-1 expression.

Fact File

Turnarounds are an application of the commutative property of addition. This property allows any number of addends to be combined in any order and the sum will always be the same.

Extend

1 Write ___ + 1 = ___ on the board. Ask the students to say numbers that will make the sentence true. For each combination, encourage the students to explain how they figured out the numbers. As the students become confident they may use numbers that are beyond the number fact range.

2 Write **15** on the board. Ask, What is fifteen add one? How do you know? Encourage the students to explain how they figured out the answer. For example, they may say, "I jumped one more than fifteen. That is sixteen." or, "When I count, I say sixteen next after fifteen." After three or four students have shared their thinking, write **15 + 1 = 16** on the board.

Repeat the activity with other starting numbers between 10 and 19. As the students become confident, extend the discussion to involve any two-digit starting number.

3 Investigate patterns for adding 1 that encourage the use of the count-on strategy. On the board, write the following number sentences:

8 + 1 = ___	9 + 1 = ___
18 + 1 = ___	19 + 1 = ___
28 + 1 = ___	29 + 1 = ___
38 + 1 = ___	39 + 1 = ___

Ask, What answers do you know? How do you know them? Encourage the students to use a variety of strategies and explain their thinking. Discuss how to use the count-on-1 strategy. Ask, What other number sentences can you write to keep the pattern going? How do you know the answers?

> ### Fact File
> A *number sentence* is a statement of the relationship between two or more expressions (e.g. 14 + 1 = 15).

4 Draw the target below on the board. Explain that scores on this target are made by adding numbers. Say, Imagine you throw two darts and one hits the middle circle and one hits somewhere on the outer ring. What is the greatest (least) score you can get?

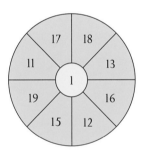

Encourage the students to explain their thinking strategies. For example, they may say, "Twenty is the greatest score you can get. Nineteen is the greatest number in the outer ring so if the second dart hits nineteen, nineteen plus one is twenty." You could also ask, If one dart hits the middle circle, how can you score fourteen? Sixteen? Nineteen? What are some other scores you can get if one dart hits the middle? Erase the numbers in the outer ring and repeat with other numbers in the 20s and 30s.

Count-on-1 Turnarounds

Introduce

1 Make a laminated "shirt" for a coat hanger as shown below. On both sides of the shirt write the numeral **5**. Attach four clothespins (pegs) on one side and one clothespin on the other and display it to the students so that the four pins are on their left-hand side.

2 Show a domino that has six dots on the left-hand side and one dot on the right as seen by the students. Select an individual to say the expression (six add one). Turn the card to change the position of the dots and ask the student to say the expression they see (one add six). The students should identify the arrangements of dots as turnarounds. Repeat with the dominoes shown below.

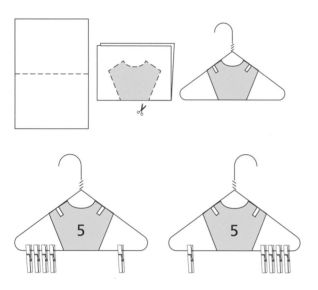

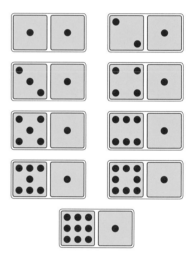

Ask, What fact can you see? (Four add one is five.) Turn the coat hanger to show the other side. Ask, What fact can you see now? (One add four is five.) What do you notice? Discuss how the parts and the totals are the same, but the order of how the parts are added has changed. Say, Four add one is the same as one add four. These are called turnaround facts. Erase the numeral on the "shirt" and repeat with other totals from 2 to 10.

3 Use the materials from the previous two activities. Give one student a domino and have them say the expression. Another student can place clothespins (pegs) on the coat hanger to show the same expression. Instruct the rest of the class to write the number fact. Direct the students with the materials to turn them around, while the rest of the class write the turnaround number fact.

Reinforce

1 Reuse the count-on strategy cards from *Introduce* Activity 4 on page 8. Select a card and display it as shown below on the left. Turn the card as shown below on the right to show the students that they can begin with either number when they add.

See: *Count-on Strategy Cards*

Ask, What do you find easier to do: start with the greater number and count on one or start with one and count on the greater number? Encourage them to explain their thinking. Demonstrate on a number track how it is easier to start with the greater number and count on 1.

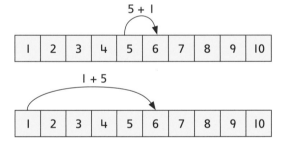

Have the students describe this count-on strategy with other cards from the set. Encourage them to start with the greater number and then count on the lesser number.

2 Make an overhead transparency of Blackline Master 11, or copy and laminate it. Write 1 in the hexagon. Ask volunteers to suggest different numbers between 1 and 9 to write in each circle. Call on other individuals to suggest numbers that can be written in each square so that, for each "spoke", the number in the circle equals the sum of the numbers in the hexagon and the square.

3 Reuse the count-on-1 flash cards from *Practice* Activity 2 on page 10 . If you made these cards, write the corresponding turnaround facts on the back of the cards as shown below. Otherwise, use the reverse side of your *Addition Flash Cards*. Copy Blackline Masters 7 and 12 and cut out the numeral cards. Display the 1 + 5 = ___ flash card and the 8 numeral card beside it. Ask, Does this make sense? Why not? Encourage the students to explain their thinking. Repeat with other pairs of matching and non-matching cards. Use addition facts that have 1 as the first addend and facts that have 1 as the second addend, so that students become familiar with the turnarounds.

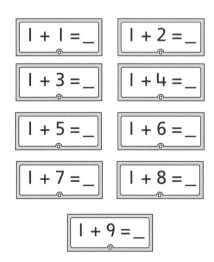

For double-sided count-on-1 cards
see: *Addition Flash Cards*

Practice

1 Reuse the count-on-1 flash cards from *Reinforce* Activity 3 on page 13. Display one card with the turnaround fact showing and select a student to say the answer. Allow a few seconds for the student to provide the answer (under three seconds is a quick response). Repeat a number of times.

2 Make a copy of Blackline Master 13 for each student. Read the instruction with the class and then direct them to complete the sheet individually.

3 Give each student a copy of Blackline Master 9 and twenty counters. Call out random count-on-1 expressions and ask the students to place a counter on each correct answer. When a student has four adjacent counters in a vertical, diagonal, or horizontal line they call out "Bingo" to win the game. The count-on expressions should range from 1 + 1 to 9 + 1, including turnarounds.

(2)	7	2	(6)	8
(5)	(3)	(8)	3	(7)
9	6	(4)	9	4
8	10	7	(5)	10
5	4	9	8	6

When a student has four adjacent counters in a vertical, diagonal, or horizontal line they call out "Bingo" to win the game.

4 Give each student a copy of Blackline Master 10 and twenty counters. Repeat the previous activity by calling out numbers from 2 to 10. This time the students place a counter on the matching expression.

Fact File
In the operation of addition, the parts that are being joined together are called *addends*. The total that they form is called the *sum*.

5 Give each student a copy of Blackline Master 14. Direct them to fold the sheet into quarters so that they can see only the *Count-On-1* section. This assessment task should take no more than two minutes for the students to complete. A longer period of time may indicate that recall of the facts is not automatic. Collect the sheets afterward and record the results for each student on Blackline Masters 1 and 2. See page 4 of the *Introduction* for instructions.

Extend

1 Write **1 +** ___ **=** ___ on the board. Ask the students to say numbers that will make the sentence true. For each combination, encourage the students to explain how they figured out the numbers. As the students become confident, they may use numbers that are beyond the number fact range.

2 Make an overhead transparency of Blackline Master 11, or copy and laminate it. Write **1** in the hexagon. Ask volunteers to suggest different numbers between 10 and 19 to write in each circle. Call on other individuals to suggest numbers that can be written in each square so that, for each "spoke", the number in the circle equals the sum of the numbers in the hexagon and the square. Repeat with other numbers from 20 to 29.

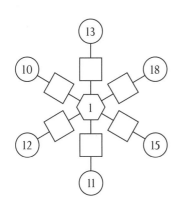

3 Write ___ **+** ___ **= 18** on the board. Ask the students to suggest a count-on-1 fact that will make the sentence true. Repeat for other totals between 10 and 30. At a later stage, repeat the activity with the sum on the left-hand side, for example, **18 =** ___ **+** ___.

Fact File

An *equation* is a number sentence that shows two expressions are equal. In simple equations like 4 + 2 = 6, writing the sum on the left-hand side (6 = 4 + 2) helps students understand that the equals symbol is not an instruction to figure out an answer. Instead, it is a way of showing equality or balance.

4 Draw the number line below on the board or on an overhead transparency. Ask, **What number could be at the start of the jump?** (Twenty-four.) **If it is twenty-four, what number will be at the other end? How do you know?** (Twenty-four count on one is twenty-five.) Redraw the "jump" arrow in a different position and repeat.

Count On 2

Introduce

1 Put five cubes into a container (e.g. a disposable cup). Write the number of cubes on the container. Hold another two cubes above the container so the students can see them and then drop them in, as shown in the diagram below. Ask, *How many cubes are in the container now? How do you know?* Repeat this activity for any starting number up to 9.

2 Draw a number track from 1 to 20 on the board. Ask a student to choose any number on the track and then instruct the rest of the class to count on from the number in steps of 2. For example, start at 3 and count 5, 7, 9, and so on. Do not count beyond 20. Repeat the activity as time allows.

3 Use the number track from the previous activity. Point to a numeral. Ask, *What is two more than this number? How do you know?* Invite volunteers to come to the board, describe their strategy, and then model the strategy on the number track. The students may suggest strategies such as, "I start at seven and jump two more to get nine." or, "When I count by twos, I know nine is the next number I say after seven." Repeat the activity frequently during the introduction of the count-on-2 strategy.

4 Select or make the count-on-2 cards shown below.

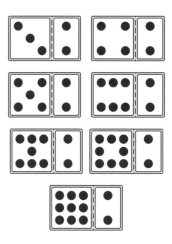

See: *Count-on Strategy Cards*

Choose a card and fold back the flap with two dots so the students cannot see it. Ask them to tell you how many dots they can see (without counting). Then fold the flap forward and ask the students to say the total number of dots. Repeat this activity several times with different cards. Vary how you hold the card so that the turnaround is sometimes used. When asked, the students should say that they start with the greater number and count on 2. Encourage them to try "jumping" to the number that is two more, rather than counting by ones.

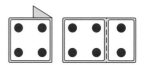

"I see four and two more. Four add two is six."

Reinforce

1 Select or make laminated, blank count-on cards. Using a non-permanent marker, create count-on-2 cards that use digits instead of dots for the greater number. Repeat *Introduce* Activity 4 on page 16 using these cards. Afterward, give each student a copy of Blackline Master 6. Instruct them to draw two dots on each card and complete the sheet.

See: *Count-on Strategy Cards*

2 Share some count-on-2 stories with the students. For example, *Four frogs are in the pond and two frogs are beside the pond. How many frogs are there in total?* Invite volunteers to suggest a different story that uses the same amounts. Encourage the students to draw and explain pictures that match their stories.

3 Make an overhead transparency of Blackline Master 11, or copy and laminate it. Write **2** in the hexagon. Ask volunteers to suggest different numbers between 3 and 9 to write in each circle. Call on other individuals to suggest numbers that can be written in each square so that, for each "spoke", the number in the circle equals the sum of the numbers in the hexagon and the square.

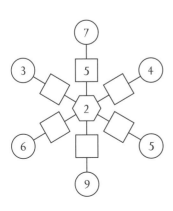

4 Give each pair of students a double ten-frame (see below), eight counters of one color and two of another color.

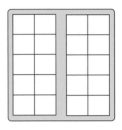

See: *Bridge-to-10 Frames*

Demonstrate how to show $6 + 2 = 8$ using the frame and counters (see below). Call out random count-on-2 expressions from $2 + 2$ to $8 + 2$ (not including turnarounds). Have the students show the two addends on different ten-frames before they move them together to show the total. The students should take turns and explain their thinking to a partner as they arrange the dots.

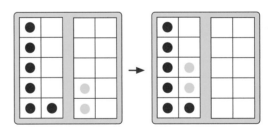

Call out, Two add four and watch what the students do and discuss. Some students may place the two amounts on separate ten-frames as before but then move the four counters onto the same frame as the two counters. Encourage them to think of the turnaround and move the lesser number.

Practice

1 ▷ Select or make double-sided count-on-2 flash cards as shown below (the turnaround fact is on the back of each card). The cards should be made of exactly the same paper as the count-on-1 cards. Show one card and invite a student to say the answer. Allow approximately three seconds for the student to provide the answer. Repeat several times with other students and cards (including the turnarounds).

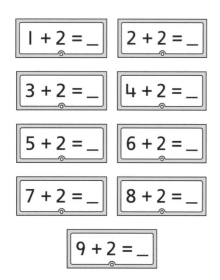

See: *Addition Flash Cards*

2 ▷ Copy Blackline Masters 7 and 12 and cut out the numeral cards. Distribute the cards with numerals from 3 to 11 to some students and the count-on-2 cards from the previous activity to others. Any remaining students can be "checkers".

Direct the students to spread out around the room. The object of this game is for the two different groups of students to form pairs to make a correct number sentence. For example, a student with the 2 + 2 = ___ card will pair up with a student with the 4 card. Once two students form a pair they should sit down.

The "checkers" can ensure that the pairs are correct. The last pair to sit down is out of the game and their cards are removed. Redistribute the cards and repeat the activity until only one pair of students remains.

Fact File

A *number* is used for counting, labeling, and ordering. The base-ten system uses ten symbols (0, 1, 2, 3, 4, 5, 6, 7, 8, 9) called *digits* to represent numbers.

A *numeral* is a single digit or combination of digits. For example, 36 is a two-digit numeral to represent the number thirty-six.

3 ▷ On the board, write the incomplete number facts shown below. The students should copy and complete the number sentences using count-on-2 facts. Encourage them to work as quickly as they can.

$$3 = \underline{} + \underline{} \qquad 4 = \underline{} + \underline{}$$
$$5 = \underline{} + \underline{} \qquad 6 = \underline{} + \underline{}$$
$$7 = \underline{} + \underline{} \qquad 8 = \underline{} + \underline{}$$
$$9 = \underline{} + \underline{} \qquad 10 = \underline{} + \underline{}$$
$$11 = \underline{} + \underline{}$$

4 ▷ Give each student a copy of Blackline Master 15. Encourage them to work quickly to complete the page. If a student finishes before others, have them select a few rows of targets and write the turnaround for each fact.

5 This is a game for two players. Give each pair of students a copy of Blackline Master 8 and a paper clip. Direct the students to straighten the paper clip to use with one of the spinners. Have them each write the numerals from 2 to 11 in a column on a sheet of paper.

To play the game:

- The first player spins the paper clip.

- The player notes where the tip of the paper clip rests and adds either 1 or 2 to that number, then loops the matching total on their sheet. If the paper clip rests on 0 or there are no available numerals the player misses that turn.

- The other player has a turn.

- The first player to loop all of their numerals wins.

6 Distribute the students' record sheets used in *Practice* Activity 5 on page 14 (Blackline Master 14). Direct them to fold the sheet so that they can see only the *Count-On-2* section. This assessment task should take no more than $1\frac{1}{2}$ minutes for the students to complete. A longer period of time may indicate that recall of the facts is not automatic. Collect the sheets afterward and record the results for each student on Blackline Masters 1 and 2. See page 4 of the *Introduction* for instructions.

Extend

1 Share some count-on-2 stories with the students. For example, Three people are in a car and two more get in. How many people are there in total? Invite volunteers to suggest a different story that uses the same amounts. Ask, What is a count-on-1 story that gives the same total? One possible example is, Four apples are in a basket and one is on the bench. How many apples are there in total?

> **Fact File**
> Addition problems can take two forms.
> *Active* problem types involve an action that is directly described or evident. In *Extend* Activity 1, the story about people in a car is active.
> The story about apples is *static* as there is no direct action. The students should be exposed to both types of problems. Active addition problems can be reversed or backtracked, so they are the best type to use for making links to subtraction.

2 Select or make the dominoes shown on page 20. Distribute the cards amongst the class. Any remaining students can be "checkers". Direct the students to spread out around the room. The object of this game is for the two different groups of students to form pairs of dominoes that have the same totals. For example, a student with a card showing two dots and three dots would pair up with a student with a card showing four dots and one dot. Once two students form a pair they should sit down. The "checkers" can ensure that the pairs are correct. The last pair to sit down is out of the game and their cards are removed. Repeat until only one pair remains.

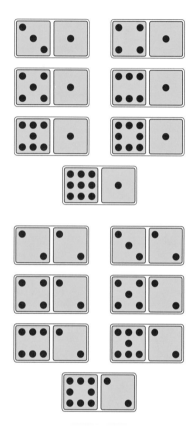

4 ▷ Give each student a double ten-frame (as shown below) and twenty counters in one color. Discuss what happens, When the fact 9 + 2 = 11 is represented on a double ten-frame, one entire ten-frame will be full and the extra counter goes on the next ten-frame.

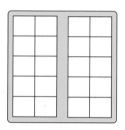

See: *Bridge-to-10 Frames*

Give each pair of students a blank cube. On the cube have them draw dots to represent 1, 2, 1, 2, 1, and 2. The aim of this game is to be the first to fill a double ten-frame exactly.

To play the game:

- The first player rolls the cube and places that number of counters on their first ten-frame.

- The other player has a turn.

- The first player rolls the cube and adds that number of counters to the counters on their ten-frame, saying the fact as they perform the addition.

- The other player has a turn.

- If a player rolls a number that will make their total number of counters exceed twenty, they miss that turn.

- The first player to fill their double ten-frame exactly is the winner.

3 ▷ Repeat the previous activity with number sentence cards. Discuss the count-on-1 and -2 expressions that are missing and write them on the board.

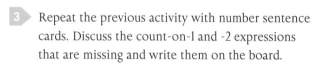

$$1 + 1 \qquad 1 + 2$$
$$2 + 1 \qquad 9 + 2$$

Ask, What do you notice about 1 + 2 and 2 + 1? (They are turnarounds.) What is the turnaround for 1 + 1? What other expressions are like 1 + 1? How are they alike? What count-on-1 expression matches 9 + 2? How do you know?

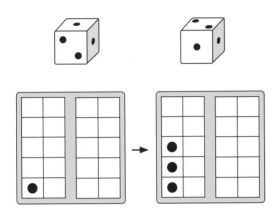

After the first roll, this player has one counter
on their ten-frame. After the second roll,
the player adds 1 + 2 and shows the total number
of counters on their ten-frame.

At different stages of the game, ask a student to
say the total number of counters on their double
ten-frame. Ask, How did you figure that out?
Responses may include, "I know that one column
of squares is five so I counted on from five." or,
"I know there is ten in one frame. I had one full
frame and two counters in the other. Ten add
two is twelve."

Fact File

An *expression* is a combination of numerals
and operation symbols (e.g. 14 + 1).

A *number sentence* is a statement of the
relationship between two or more expressions
(e.g. 14 + 1 = 15).

5 On the board or an overhead transparency, draw
two large grids of numbers as shown below. Ask
the students to choose one number from each
grid and give the total. Encourage the students to
explain their thinking strategies. Cover the two
numbers that are chosen. Repeat the discussion
until both grids are covered. Erase the numbers on
the left-hand side and repeat with numbers in the
30s and 40s. Only use numbers that do not bridge
across ten (for example, do not use 39 + 2 = 41).
The numbers do not have to be in sequence.

20	21	22
23	24	25
26	27	28

1	1	1
2	2	2
1	2	1

6 Use the grids from the previous activity. Cover
a number 1 in the grid shown on the right. Ask,
What number in the other grid can be added to
one to make twenty-eight? How do you know?
Encourage the students to explain their thinking.
Cover a number 2 and repeat the questions. Repeat
the activity as time allows.

Count On 3

Introduce

1 Make an overhead transparency of a double ten-frame and place counters on it as shown below. Ask, **What is four add three? How do you know?** Ask individuals to explain their thinking and move the counters to demonstrate. For example, they may say, "I know four add one is five. I have two left. Five add two is seven. So four add three is seven." Repeat with starting numbers from 3 to 9. Point out that some count-on-3 facts (such as $1 + 3 = 4$ and $2 + 3 = 5$) are also turnarounds for the count-on-1 and count-on-2 facts.

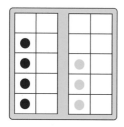

2 Draw a number track from 1 to 20 on the board. Point to a number and ask, **What is three more than this number? How do you know?** Invite volunteers to describe and then act out their strategy on the number track. The students may suggest strategies such as, "I start at seven and jump three more to get ten." or, "I start at seven and jump two, then one more." Repeat the activity frequently during the introduction of the count-on-3 strategy.

3 Select or make the count-on-3 cards shown below.

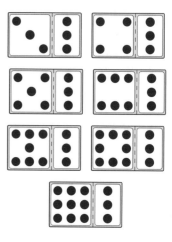

See: *Count-on Strategy Cards*

Choose a card and fold back the flap with three dots so the students cannot see it (see the diagram below). Ask them to tell you how many dots they can see (without counting). Then fold the flap forward and ask the students to say the total number of dots. Repeat this activity several times with different cards. Vary how you hold the card so that the turnaround is sometimes used. When asked, the students should say that they start with the greater number and count on 3. Encourage them to try "jumping" to the number that is 3 more, rather than actually counting by ones. Be aware that some students may not be able to count on 3 as easily as they can count on 1 or 2.

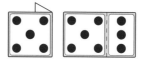

"I see five and three more. Five add three is eight."

Reinforce

1 Select or make laminated, blank count-on cards. Using a non-permanent marker, create count-on-3 cards that use digits instead of dots for the greater number. Repeat *Introduce* Activity 3 on page 22 using these cards. Afterward, give each student a copy of Blackline Master 6. Instruct the students to draw three dots on each card and write the new numbers.

See: Count-on Strategy Cards

2 Direct the students to write some count-on-3 stories. For example, Five bags are on the floor and three are on the table. How many bags are there in total? Invite an individual to share a count-on-3 story with the rest of the class. Ask, Does anyone else have a story that describes the same count-on-3 fact? Who can tell me a story that involves the turnaround of this count-on-3 fact?

3 Make an overhead transparency of Blackline Master 11, or copy and laminate it. Write **3** in the hexagon. Ask volunteers to suggest different numbers between 4 and 9 to write in each circle. Call on other individuals to suggest numbers that can be written in each square so that, for each "spoke", the number in the circle equals the sum of the numbers in the hexagon and the square.

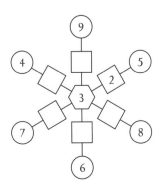

4 Make or select the double-sided count-on-3 cards shown below (the turnaround fact is on the back of each card). The cards should be made of exactly the same paper as the other flash cards used previously.

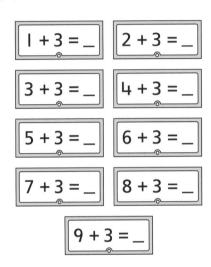

See: Addition Flash Cards

Copy Blackline Masters 7 and 12 and cut out the numeral cards. Display the 5 + 3 = ___ flash card with the 7 numeral card beside it. Ask, Does this make sense? Why not? Encourage the students to explain their thinking. Repeat with other pairs of matching and non-matching cards.

5 Ask a small group of students to sort the dominoes shown below into matching pairs according to the total number of dots. For example, the dominoes showing 5 + 2 and 4 + 3 both have a total of 7.

Discuss how two of the dominoes do not have pairs. Ask, Why doesn't the domino with two dots and three dots have a partner? (It shows two facts on the one card: two add three and three add two.) What is a count-on fact to match nine add three? (Ten add two.)

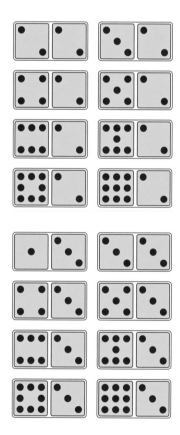

Practice

1 Copy Blackline Masters 7 and 12 and cut out the numeral cards. Distribute the cards with numerals from 4 to 12 to some students and the count-on-3 cards used in from *Reinforce* Activity 4 on page 23 to others. Any remaining students can be "checkers". The object of this game is for the two different groups of students to form pairs to make a correct number sentence. For example, a student with the 3 + 3 = ___ flash card pairs up with a student with the 6 numeral card. Once two students form a pair, have them sit down. The "checkers" can ensure that the pairs are correct. The last pair to sit down is out of the game. Repeat until only one pair of students remains.

2 Reuse the count-on-3 cards from the previous activity. Show one card and invite a student to say the answer. Allow a few seconds for the student to provide the answer (under three seconds is a quick response). The students should be able to describe how they started with the greater number to figure out 1 + 3 = ___ and 2 + 3 = ___. Repeat several times.

3 Make a copy of Blackline Master 16 for each student. Read the instructions and then direct the students to complete the sheet individually.

Fact File

A *number* is used for counting, labeling, and ordering. The base-ten system uses ten symbols (0, 1, 2, 3, 4, 5, 6, 7, 8, 9) called *digits* to represent numbers.

A *numeral* is a single digit or combination of digits. For example, 36 is a two-digit numeral to represent the number thirty-six.

4 This is a game for two players. Give each student a copy of Blackline Master 17 and each pair of students two blank cubes. Have the students draw dots to represent 1, 2, 3, 1, 2, and 3 on one cube and write the numerals 4, 5, 6, 7, 8, and 9 on the other. Instruct the students to underline the 6 and 9 to avoid confusion.

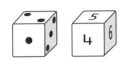

To play the game:

- The first player rolls both cubes and adds the two numbers.

- The player finds the matching total on their sheet and writes the number fact, starting with the greater number.

- The other player has a turn.

- As the game continues, the player misses a turn if the total rolled does not match any of the unused totals on the sheet.

- The player who completes their sheet first is the winner.

5 Give each pair of students a copy of Blackline Master 18 and fifty counters (twenty-five of two colors). Instruct the students to copy the dot cube from the previous activity so that they have two dot cubes. Then have them label a third cube with the numerals 2, 3, 4, 2, 3, and 4.

To play the game:

- Players sit at opposite ends of their game board.

- The first player rolls all three cubes. They then select a dot cube to add to the numeral cube so that the total matches a "tower" on the game board. The player places one counter on each tile of the matching "tower", using different colors to represent the two numbers that were added. If no "towers" are empty for either number fact shown on the cubes, the player misses that turn.

- The other player has a turn.

- The first player to fill all of their "towers" is the winner.

After this roll, the player can make a total of 5 (3 + 2) or 6 (3 + 3).

At different stages, point to an empty "tower" and ask, What numbers can you roll to make that total? What other numbers can you roll to make that total? If you roll a four, what number will you need to roll on a dot cube to fill a "tower"?

6 Distribute the students' record sheets from *Practice Activity 5* on page 14 (Blackline Master 14). Direct them to fold the sheet so that they can see only the *Count-On-3* section. This assessment task should take no more than $1\frac{1}{2}$ minutes for the students to complete. A longer period of time may indicate that recall of the facts is not automatic. Collect the sheets afterward and record the results for each student on Blackline Masters 1 and 2. See page 4 of the *Introduction* for instructions.

Extend

1 Draw the diagram shown below on the board. Explain that the number written in the middle is the total for three count-on facts. Call on volunteers to suggest the count-on-1, count-on-2, and count-on-3 expressions that match and write them in the correct spaces.

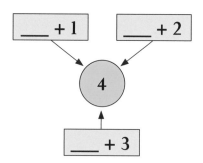

Have the students choose five different totals from 5 to 12. Instruct them to write the three expressions that match each total. Afterward, confident students may like to try totals greater than 12.

2 Investigate patterns for adding 3 that encourage the use of the count-on strategy. On the board, write the following number sentences:

6 + 3 = ___	7 + 3 = ___	8 + 3 = ___
16 + 3 = ___	17 + 3 = ___	18 + 3 = ___
26 + 3 = ___	27 + 3 = ___	28 + 3 = ___
36 + 3 = ___	37 + 3 = ___	38 + 3 = ___

Ask, Which answers do you know? How do you know them? Encourage the students to use a variety of strategies and explain their thinking. Discuss how to use the count-on-3 strategy. Ask, What other number sentences can you write to keep the pattern going? How do you know the answers?

3 Draw the target below on the board. Explain that scores on this target are made by adding two numbers. Say, Imagine you throw two darts and one hits the middle circle and one hits the outer ring. What is the greatest (or least) score you can get?

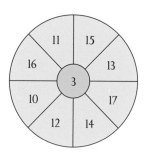

Encourage the students to explain their thinking strategies. For example, they may say, "Twenty is the greatest score you can get. Seventeen is the greatest number in the outer ring. So if the second dart hits seventeen, seventeen plus three is twenty." Ask, If one dart hits the middle circle, how can you score fourteen? Sixteen? Nineteen? What are some other scores you can get if one dart hits the middle of the target? Afterward, erase the numbers in the outer ring and repeat with other numbers in the 20s, 30s, and 40s.

Count On 0

Introduce

1 Many students find it difficult to comprehend what zero means. The activities on this page help develop the idea of zero. Write **0** and **zero** on the board. Ask students to suggest other words for zero. Write their suggestions on the board. Examples may include, none, nothing, nil, empty, nought, all gone, and no more.

Discuss real-world situations in which zero might be used. For example, We bought a bag of four potatoes. We used them all to make soup. The bag was empty. Encourage the students to explain where zero is used in this story.

> ### Fact File
> The idea of zero is complex. Historically, it took a long time for people to create a symbol to represent nothing. The symbol we use today (0) has its origins in numerals developed in India during the sixth century A.D.

2 Adding zero is often a new experience for students. The conceptual development for addition (and the other operations) involving zero does not usually include real-world stories or the manipulation of concrete materials. One useful introduction to this strategy is to create some contextual stories that involve adding zero.

Write several addition facts that involve zero on the board (e.g. $5 + 0 = 5$). Next, share a story that might happen out of school. For example, My brother gave me five chocolate bars. My sister did not give me any chocolate. I now have five chocolate bars. Have the students select a fact from the board, write a story and draw a picture to match. Encourage them to share their stories with the class.

3 Write a number fact on the board that involves counting on 1, 2, 3, or 0. Direct the students to use cubes of two different colors to make a cube train that shows the fact. Repeat as time allows, making sure that all types of count-on facts are covered.

4 Select or make laminated, blank count-on cards. Using a non-permanent marker, create count-on-0 cards for $1 + 0$ to $9 + 0$ like the example shown below. Select one card, fold back the flap and ask the students to say how many dots there are. Fold the flap forward and ask them to tell you what the card shows. It might help to have the students write the fact they see on the card. Write the fact on the board and repeat the process using other cards. Then turn each card to show that the turnaround idea also works for zero.

"I see four and no more. Four add zero is four."

> ### Fact File
> Only three ancient cultures developed a symbol for zero: the Maya, Babylonians, and Hindus. The Hindu symbol, a small circle, was adapted and introduced into Europe by Arab merchants. The word *zero* reveals the same path as the symbol: it comes from the Arabic word *sifr*, which is a translation of the Hindu word *sunya*, meaning "empty" or "nothing".

Reinforce

1 Write the incomplete number sentences shown below on the board. Instruct the students to copy and complete them. They can then draw a cube train to match each one, using two different pencils to shade the parts. Repeat with other number facts as time allows.

$$5 + 0 = \underline{\quad} \qquad 2 + 5 = \underline{\quad} \qquad 1 + 4 = \underline{\quad}$$

$$7 + 0 = \underline{\quad} \qquad 3 + 2 = \underline{\quad} \qquad 8 + 1 = \underline{\quad}$$

$$0 + 6 = \underline{\quad} \qquad 2 + 6 = \underline{\quad}$$

A cube train showing 1 + 4 = 5.

2 Make a copy of Blackline Master 7 and cut out the numeral cards. Select or make the count-on-0 flash cards shown below (the turnaround fact is on the back of each card). Display one of the cards and invite a volunteer to select the matching numeral card. Repeat with other count-on cards and different students. Be sure to include turnaround facts. Afterward, choose numeral cards and have students identify the count-on-0 card that matches.

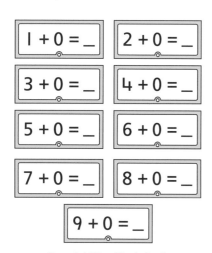

See: *Addition Flash Cards*

3 The students can work in pairs for this activity. Give each pair a copy of Blackline Master 8 and a paper clip. Direct the students to cut out one of the spinners and straighten part of the paper clip as shown below. One student spins the paper clip and says the number that the tip eventually rests on. The other student writes an addition fact using this number and 0. This is repeated until the student has written six different number facts. The players then change roles and repeat the activity.

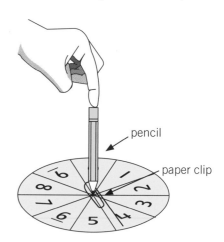

4 Draw or make an overhead transparency of one of the spinners on Blackline Master 8. Say, Imagine you throw two darts at this target. What are all of the different ways to get a score of nine? How do you know? Encourage the students to explain their thinking. Repeat the discussion for other totals.

As the students develop confidence, ask other questions such as, If you throw two darts at this target, what scores (other than ten) can you get in only one way? How do you know? If one dart has hit two, what is the greatest score you can get after throwing the second dart? How do you know? Challenge the students to make up their own questions that involve adding 0, 1, 2, or 3 to any of the other numbers on the target.

Practice

1. Make a copy of Blackline Master 19 for each student. Read the instruction and then direct the students to complete the sheet individually.

2. Make or select the count-on flash cards from the following activities:

   - *Reinforce* Activity 3 on page 13
   - *Practice* Activity 1 on page 18
   - *Reinforce* Activity 4 on page 23
   - *Reinforce* Activity 2 on page 28

   Display one of the cards and invite a student to say the total. Allow a few seconds for the student to provide the answer. Repeat several times with other students and cards (including turnarounds).

3. This is a game for two teams. Copy Blackline Masters 7 and 12 and cut out the numeral cards from 2 to 12. Make or select the sets of dominoes from *Introduce* Activity 2 on page 12 and *Reinforce* Activity 5 on page 23. One domino (1 + 3) will already be present as a turnaround (3 + 1). Also, make dominoes that show the number facts from 1 + 0 to 9 + 0.

   To play the game:

   - The dominoes are placed facedown and mixed around. The teams take turns to pick an equal number of dominoes, keeping them facedown. Any extra dominoes are placed to one side.

   - The numeral cards are spread out face up in a line between the two teams.

   - At a starting time the teams work quickly to match their dominoes to the numeral cards. The students should ensure their dominoes stay on their team's side of the numeral cards.

   - Once both teams are finished, all players check the matching for accuracy. All the correct matches for each team are placed to one side.

   - The first team to finish the matching earns five points. Then each team earns one bonus point for each correct match.

   - The team with the most points wins.

4. A variation of the previous activity is to allow the students to work in pairs with a stop watch. One student selects ten dominoes. When their partner starts the stop watch, they are to match the dominoes to the numeral cards as quickly as possible. Once finished, their partner checks that the matching is correct. Students may wish to compete against each other for fastest times, or against themselves for their "personal best".

5. Distribute the students' record sheets used in *Practice* Activity 5 on page 14 (Blackline Master 14). Direct them to fold the sheet so that they can see only the *Count-On-0* section. This assessment task should take no more than about $1\frac{1}{2}$ minutes for the students to complete. A longer period of time may indicate that recall of the facts is not automatic. Collect the sheets afterward and record the results for each student on Blackline Masters 1 and 2. See page 4 of the *Introduction* for instructions.

Extend

1 Draw a number track from 0 to 20 on the ground, making each square large enough for a student to stand in. Arrange students to stand on the numerals 0, 3, 6, 9, 12, 15, and 18. Call out, Count on one and have the students move forward one square. Direct the students to return to their starting position and repeat for counting on 2. After they return to their original position say, Count on zero. What happens? (Everyone stays in their position.) Ask, What will happen when I call out "count on three"? (All students except one will take the place of the person in front of them. The student on eighteen will move off the track.) On what number would the student on eighteen finish if the track was longer?

Continue using different count-on combinations of 0, 1, 2, and 3. As students step beyond 20, instruct them to stand to the side and a new student can start on 0.

Fact File
Using a clock face to perform mathematical operations such as addition produces interesting results. For example counting on 3 from 10 gives a result of 1, not 13. Adding 8 and 7 gives a result of 3, not 15. Operations on clocks are part of a branch of mathematics called modular arithmetic. Together with prime numbers, *modular arithmetic* is the foundation for current internet security.

2 Copy Blackline Master 12 and cut out the numeral cards. Display a card and ask, What number is two more than this? How do you know? Encourage several students in the class to describe the strategies they used to figure out the answer. Repeat the activity, asking the students to count on 0, 1, 2, or 3 each time.

3 Draw two large grids as shown below on the board or an overhead transparency. Ask the students to choose one number from each grid and give the total. Encourage them to explain how they know the answer. Cover the two numbers that were chosen. Repeat the discussion until both grids are covered. Keep the grids for further discussion.

30	31	32	33
34	35	36	37
38	39	40	41
42	43	44	45

0	1	2	3
0	1	2	3
0	1	2	3
0	1	2	3

4 Reuse the grids from the previous activity. Cover a number 2 in the grid shown at the right. Ask, What number in the other grid will add to two to make forty-one? How do you know? Cover the number the students suggest as they explain their thinking. Then cover a number 1 and repeat the questions. Repeat starting with 0, 1, 2, or 3 in the grid on the right.

5 Give each student a copy of Blackline Master 20. Explain how to shade a number in each wheel, then count on 0, 1, 2, and 3 and write the number facts. The students should shade a different number in each wheel.

Use Doubles

The use-doubles strategy includes those facts that involve doubling a number. Most students learn these facts easily, due to their natural curiosity and fascination with numbers that are the same. However, there is still a need to check that all students can recall the answers quickly. The use-doubles facts also include the double-plus-1 and double-plus-2 facts. When students know the doubles, it is not difficult for them to add on 1 or 2. To do this they need to know which facts fit the strategy and which doubles to use to help them with these facts.

Fact File
The use-doubles strategy is also known as the *near-doubles* strategy.

Prepare

1. Check that the students understand the "teen" numbers and that they can record them in symbol form. Ensure that they can write the "teen" numbers when they hear or say the number name.

2. Review what the students know about odd and even numbers. The students should understand that even numbers can be split into two equal amounts. Say different numbers less than 10. Direct the students to represent each number using counters and then ask them to split the counters for each number into two equal groups. Ask them to identify each starting number as odd or even.

3. Choose a number that is less than 10. Invite a volunteer to count by twos from that number. Afterward, have them identify whether the sequence involved even numbers or odd numbers. Repeat with other numbers and students.

Double

Introduce

1 Review the count-on facts that the students know. Draw the dominoes shown below on the board and ask, **What do you notice about these count-on facts?** (Each one has parts that are the same.) **What is a double? What are some other doubles you know? Where do you see doubles in everyday life?** The students may provide examples such as hands, feet, dominoes, and egg cartons.

The students can draw or cut pictures out from magazines to match the examples they gave. Instruct the students to label each picture with the double fact that matches, for example, Double 3 is 6. Display the students' work around the classroom. Ensure that examples for each doubles fact from double 1 to double 9 are shown.

"Double 2 is 4."

"Double 5 is 10."

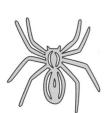

"Double 4 is 8."

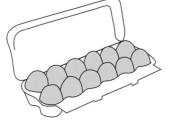

"Double 6 is 12."

2 Use the students' pictures from the previous activity to help them describe the double facts. For example, cover up one side of the horse and ask, **If there are two legs on one side of the horse, how many legs are on the other side?** (Two.) **How many are two and two? What is another way of saying two and two?** (Double two.)

3 Have the students use paint and paper to make doubling patterns. Instruct the students to fold a sheet of paper in half and open it out again. Instruct them to put paint blobs on one side of the sheet. By folding the paper in half again they will see that they have doubled the number of paint blobs. The students can then write a description of what they did below their picture.

I have made 8 by doubling 4.

4 ▷ Make an overhead transparency of a double ten-frame and place counters on it as shown below. Ask the class to predict what the double of the number will be and ask individuals to explain their thinking. If necessary, a matching number of counters can be placed on the other ten-frame then moved to the first frame to check the prediction. Students may provide explanations such as, "I know double five is ten because I have five fingers on each hand. Double four is like folding a finger down on each hand, so four and four is eight." or, "Double four is the same as five add three, which is eight." Repeat the activity for other numbers up to double 5.

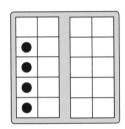

Fact File

The word *double* comes from the Latin word *duplus*. This is a combination of *duo*, meaning "two", and *plus*, which means "fold". When something is folded over itself there are twice as many layers as before. *Two-fold* is a direct translation still used today. Examples of related words are a *duplex* apartment (a two-storey residence) and *duplicate* (to make two of something).

5 ▷ Select or make the doubles cards shown below.

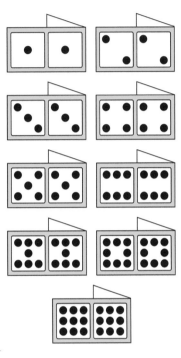

See: *Use-Doubles Strategy Cards*

Choose a card and cover one arrangement of dots with a sheet of paper as shown below. Ask, **How many dots are there? How many dots will there be if we double this number?** Invite volunteers to explain their thinking before uncovering the dots and confirming the total. Rotate a card 180° and ask, **What do you notice about the turnarounds for doubles?** (They are exactly the same as the original fact.)

Reinforce

1. Select or make a laminated, blank double card. Choose one of the double facts from *Introduce* Activity 5 on page 33. Write the numerals instead of dots on the blank card. Repeat the activity as before.

2. Give each student a copy of Blackline Master 21. Instruct the students to complete each picture before writing the double fact. Fast finishers may like to create other pictures for other doubles and write the matching number facts.

3. Draw a number track from 1 to 20 on the board. Point to 12 and ask, What double fact has twelve as a total? Encourage the students to explain how they know. Next, point to 15 and ask, Is there a double fact that has fifteen as a total? How do you know? Repeat this for other randomly selected numbers on the track.

Fact File

A *number track* is a useful model for the idea of counting discrete quantities. For example, the number of apples in a bag.

A *number line* is useful for modeling the idea of measuring continuous quantities to different degrees of precision. For example, mass can be measured in whole kilograms, grams, milligrams, and so on, becoming more precise as smaller units are used.

---

4. Draw two number tracks from 1 to 20 inclusive on the board. The top track shows the numbers to double, while the lower track shows the totals. Point to 1 in the top track and say, Double one is two. Cross out the 1 in the top track and the 2 in the lower track. Ask, What is double two? Cross out the 2 and the 4. Repeat for double 3, double 4, and double 5. Ask, What do you notice about the two tracks? Bring out the fact that odd numbers are missed out along the lower track. Highlight, that for every one space that is moved along on the top track, two are moved along the lower track.

5. Write **15** on the board. Ask, What numbers can you double so the answer is less than fifteen? How do you know? Encourage the students to explain their thinking. Repeat the activity for other numbers between 12 and 20.

6. On the board, draw the grid shown below. Point to one of the numerals and ask the students to suggest a double that matches. Ask, What count-on fact has the same total? The students should be able to provide a count-on-1, count-on-2, or count-on-3 fact to match. Choose another number and repeat.

2	8	12
14	4	10
18	16	6

Practice

1. Select or make doubles flash cards as shown below. The cards should be made of exactly the same paper as the other flash cards used previously. Some of the cards will have been used to teach other facts. Display one card and invite a student to say the answer. Allow approximately three seconds for the student to provide the answer. Repeat several times with other students and cards.

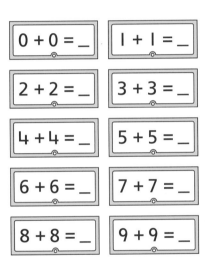

See: *Addition Flash Cards*

2. Give each student a copy of Blackline Master 22. Make sure they understand that they shade only the double facts. The students should complete the sheet individually.

3. Give each pair of students a copy of Blackline Master 23 and twenty counters. Call out a random number from 0 to 18 and ask the students to place a counter on each matching expression. When a student has four adjacent counters in a diagonal, horizontal, or vertical line, they call out "Bingo" to win the game.

4. This is a game for two players. Each student will need four counters (a different color for each student). Provide each pair with a copy of Blackline Master 24 and a blank cube. Instruct the students to write the numerals 4, 5, 6, 7, 8, and 9 on the cube. The 6 and 9 should be underlined to avoid confusion. Draw the grid shown below on the board and direct one student in each group to copy it onto their grid.

16	14	8
10	18	12
14	8	10
18	12	16

To play the game:

- The first player rolls the cube.

- The player then doubles the numeral shown and covers the total on the grid with one of their counters.

- The other player has a turn.

- As the game continues, the player misses a turn if the total has already been covered.

- The first player to place all four counters on the grid wins.

As the students play the game, ask questions such as, What do you need to roll to place a counter on that total?

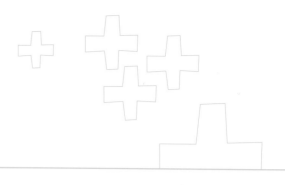

5 ▷ Give each pair of students a stop watch, a set of the dominoes shown below, and the numeral cards from Blackline Masters 7 and 12. Together, they should select numeral cards that show the even numbers. These cards are then arranged face up in a row. The dominoes are turned facedown and mixed around. When their partner starts the stop watch, the first student turns the dominoes over and matches them to the numeral cards as quickly as possible. Once finished, their partner checks that the matching is correct. Students may wish to compete against each other for the fastest times, or against themselves for their "personal best".

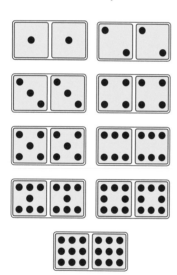

6 ▷ Give each student a copy of Blackline Master 25. Direct them to fold the sheet into quarters so that they can see only the *Double* section. This assessment task should take approximately one minute for the students to complete. A longer period of time may indicate that recall of the facts is not automatic. Collect the sheets afterward and record the results for each student on Blackline Masters 1 and 2. See page 4 of the *Introduction* for instructions.

Extend

1 ▷ Investigate doubling numbers beyond the number fact range. Begin with numbers that are multiples of 10. Write on the board:

$$10 + 10 = \underline{\quad}$$

$$20 + 20 = \underline{\quad}$$

$$30 + 30 = \underline{\quad}$$

$$40 + 40 = \underline{\quad}$$

Ask, What are the totals? How do you know? Encourage the students to use a variety of explanations. For example, they may say, "Forty is four tens. Four tens and four tens is eight tens. The answer to forty add forty is eighty." or, "I know forty is like four, so double forty is eighty just like double four is eight."

2 ▷ Write the number sentences shown below on the board. Encourage the students to explain a variety of thinking strategies they can use to help them figure out the answers. For example, "Double ten is twenty and double three is six, so double thirteen is twenty-six." Repeat with other numbers from 20 to 24 or from 30 to 34. In this way, the students can double without regrouping.

$$10 + 10 = \underline{\quad}$$

$$11 + 11 = \underline{\quad}$$

$$12 + 12 = \underline{\quad}$$

$$13 + 13 = \underline{\quad}$$

$$14 + 14 = \underline{\quad}$$

Fact File

Regrouping involves exchanging a quantity in one place (e.g. tens) for an amount in another (e.g. hundreds). For example, 12 tens can be regrouped as 1 hundred and 2 tens.

3 Invite the students to complete doubling sequences. Write **1** on the board. Ask, What is double one? Can you keep doubling? How far can you go? Write each number on the board in sequence, then pause and ask the students to explain how they know the double. Stop when the students seem unsure about the next double.

1   2   4   8   16   32   64

Repeat the activity starting with 2 then 3.

2   4   8   16   32   64

3   6   12   24   48

Work with the class to complete the sequences starting with 4, 5, and 6, as shown below.

4   8   16   32   64

5   10   20   40   80

6   12   24   48

Ask, What rows have the same numbers in them? What do you think will happen if you continue these rows? (All the numbers in the row starting with four are in the rows starting with two and one. Similarly, the numbers in the row starting with six are in the row starting with three.) At another time, repeat the activity and ask, Which rows do not have any of the same numbers?

Double Plus 1

Introduce

1 ▷ Make two cube trains as shown below and show them to the students. Ask, What number fact do these show? (Four add five.) What do you notice about this fact? (It is almost a double.) So what facts can you use to figure out the total? The students should explain that they can either double 4 and count on 1, or double 5 and count back 1.

2 ▷ Write the following number sentences on the board:

$$4 + 5 = \underline{}$$

$$8 + 7 = \underline{}$$

$$3 + 2 = \underline{}$$

$$5 + 6 = \underline{}$$

Instruct the students to copy the sentences and loop the lesser addend in each one. Identification of the lesser addend is the first step in using the double-plus-1 strategy, so check that the students can complete this task quickly and accurately. Repeat with other double-plus-1 facts.

3 ▷ Select or make the double-plus-1 cards shown below (the dotted circles indicate what is on the back of the flap).

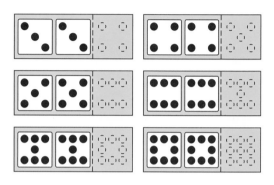

See: *Use-Doubles Strategy Cards*

Hold the 4 + 5 card so that the flap with five dots is folded back on the right-hand side as seen by the students. Ask, What fact do you see? (Double four.) How many dots are there in total? (Eight.)

Fold the flap forward so that the five dots cover four dots. Ask, How many dots are there now? How do you know? Repeat with other cards, including turnarounds.

4 ▷ Give the students twenty-one connecting cubes of three colors (e.g. ten green, ten blue, one red). Have the students use their cubes to make a train that shows a double-plus-1 fact. Instruct them to write the number fact their cubes show and then repeat the activity for another fact.

Reinforce

1. Tell some double-plus-1 stories and have the students act them out. For example, Four people are sitting down and five are standing up. How many people are there in total? How do you know? Encourage the students to each write a double-plus-1 story to share with the rest of the class.

2. Write these number sentences on the board:

$$4 + 5 = \underline{\quad}$$

$$4 + 4 + 1 = \underline{\quad}$$

Ask, How do you know these number sentences have the same answer? Encourage the students to give more than one explanation. Then ask, What are some other number sentences that use four, four, and one to give the same answer? How do you know they have the same answer? Encourage the students to suggest the other two number sentences that use 4, 4, and 1 to make a total of 9 ($4 + 1 + 4 = 9$ and $1 + 4 + 4 = 9$). Repeat with other double-plus-1 facts.

3. Write the numerals 1 to 20 on the board. Say, Choose a number between one and ten. When you double this number, what total do you get? As the students identify the doubles, draw a ✓ above each numeral.

✓ ✓ ✓ ✓ ✓ ✓ ✓ ✓ ✓ ✓
1 2 3 4 5 6 7 8 9 10 11 12 13 14 15 16 17 18 19 20

Ask, When you double and add one to your number, what total do you get? How do you know? As the students identify the totals, draw a ✗ below each numeral.

✓ ✓ ✓ ✓ ✓ ✓ ✓ ✓ ✓ ✓
1 2 3 4 5 6 7 8 9 10 11 12 13 14 15 16 17 18 19 20
✗ ✗ ✗ ✗ ✗ ✗ ✗ ✗ ✗

Ask the students to describe what they notice. Encourage a variety of observations. For example, "Double facts have totals that are even numbers and double-plus-1 facts have totals that are odd numbers."

4. Draw a vertical number track on the board as partly shown below. Ask, What is the double fact that has a total of twelve? Write = 6 + 6 beside 12 on the number track. Ask, What is the double fact that has a total of fourteen? Write = 7 + 7 beside 14. Ask, What number is "sandwiched" between twelve and fourteen? (Thirteen.) What is a double-plus-1 fact that has that total? Write = 6 + 7 beside 13 and ask the students to describe what they notice about the three facts. Bring out that, because the total for 6 + 7 is more than 6 + 6 and less than 7 + 7, it must be between 12 and 14. Repeat with other numbers shown on the track.

11	
12	= 6 + 6
13	= 6 + 7
14	= 7 + 7
15	

Practice

1 ▶ Select or make a set of double-sided cards for the double-plus-1 facts shown below (the turnaround fact is on the back of each card). You will have used some of the cards previously to teach other facts. Randomly select a card and show it to the class for approximately three seconds. Have the students write or say the answer. Repeat with other cards.

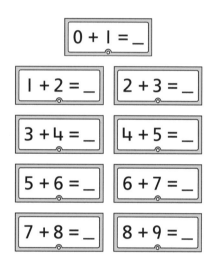

0 + 1 = _

1 + 2 = _	2 + 3 = _
3 + 4 = _	4 + 5 = _
5 + 6 = _	6 + 7 = _
7 + 8 = _	8 + 9 = _

See: *Addition Flash Cards*

2 ▶ This is a game for two players. Each student will need four counters (a different color for each student). Provide each group with a copy of Blackline Master 24 and a blank cube. On the cube have the students write the numerals 3, 4, 5, 6, 7, and 8. The 6 should be underlined to avoid confusion. Draw the grid shown below on the board and direct one student in each group to copy it onto the top half of their grid.

11	7	15
17	9	11
7	13	17
15	9	13

To play the game:

- The first player rolls the cube.

- The player then doubles the numeral shown and adds 1, and covers the total on the grid with one of their counters.

- The other player has a turn.

- As the game continues, the player misses a turn if the total has already been covered.

- The first player to place all four counters on the grid wins.

3 ▶ This variation of the previous activity involves double and double-plus-1 facts. Reuse the materials from the previous activity. Direct one student in each group to copy the grid below onto the lower half of their grid. Give each student an extra four counters and provide each group with an additional blank cube. Instruct the students to write "plus 1" on three of the faces. The other three faces should be left blank. The students play the game as before, except they roll two cubes. If the second cube shows a blank face then the students double the number. If it shows "plus 1", the students double the number then add 1. The first player to place eight counters on the grid is the winner.

7	11	15	6	10	12
13	8	12	16	8	11
16	14	9	13	17	9
6	17	15	10	14	18

4 Give each student a copy of Blackline Master 26. Ensure they understand that they shade only the totals that are even numbers. The students should complete the sheet individually.

5 This is a game for two players. Give each pair of students a copy of Blackline Master 8 and a paper clip. Direct the students to cut out one spinner and straighten part of the paper clip as shown below.

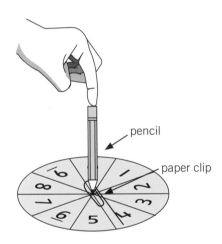

pencil

paper clip

Each pair of students should write the numerals 1, 3, 5, 7, 9, 11, 13, 15, 17, and 19 in a row on a sheet of paper.

To play the game:

• The first player spins the paper clip.

• The player notes where the tip of the paper clip rests and doubles that number and adds 1. The player draws a ✓ under the matching total in the row of numerals.

• The other player has a turn but draws a ✓ above the row of numerals.

• As the game continues, the player misses a turn if a ✓ has already been drawn for the total.

• The first player to draw three ✓ in a row wins.

```
      ✓  ✓  ✓           ✓
  1   3  5  7  9  11  13  15  17  19
         ✓     ✓           ✓
```

As the students play the game, ask questions such as, What number do you need to spin to mark this total? What number do you need to spin to win the game?

6 Distribute the students' record sheets used in *Practice* Activity 6 on page 36 (Blackline Master 25). Direct them to fold the sheet so that they can see only the *Double-Plus-1* section. This assessment task should take no more than $1\frac{1}{2}$ minutes for the students to complete. A longer period of time may indicate that recall of the facts is not automatic. Collect the sheets afterward and record the results for each student on Blackline Masters 1 and 2. See page 4 of the *Introduction* for instructions.

Extend

1 When the students are confident with the strategy for doubling and adding 1 for numbers less than 10, they can try using numbers greater than 10. For the first examples, use numbers that are slightly greater than multiples of 10, for example, 21 or 31. Write the following number sentences on the board:

$$20 + 20 = \underline{\quad}$$

$$20 + 21 = \underline{\quad}$$

$$21 + 20 = \underline{\quad}$$

Ask the students to explain how they can use the first number sentence to help them figure out the answers to the other two number sentences. Repeat the discussion with other sets of three related number sentences that are near a double. Later, number sentences close to a double can be used without the double to assist them. For example, $41 + 40 = \underline{\quad}$ or $30 + 31 = \underline{\quad}$.

2 Repeat the previous activity using other numbers that the students can double easily or numbers close to a number they can double easily. For example:

$$13 + 14 = \underline{\quad}$$

$$24 + 25 = \underline{\quad}$$

$$32 + 33 = \underline{\quad}$$

Ask the students to suggest other number sentences they can use a double to answer.

3 After the students are confident with doubling and adding 1, discuss subtracting 1 from a double.

Write $11 + 12 = \underline{\quad}$ on the board. Ask, What is the total? How do you know? Encourage the students to suggest a variety of strategies. One of the goals of this discussion is to interpret a number sentence in two different ways. For example, students may think, "Ten and ten add one and two is twenty and three or twenty-three." or, "Double ten and three is twenty-three." Encourage the students to share different ways a double might help them figure out the answer. For example, the students may double 12 and subtract 1 or double 11 and add 1.

On the board, write a summary of the thinking the students use to help figure out the answers. Include number sentences in the written descriptions. For example:

$$11 + 12 = \underline{\quad}$$

$$\text{is } 12 + 12 - 1 = \underline{\quad}$$

$$\text{or } 10 + 10 + 1 + 2 = \underline{\quad}$$

4 Write $\underline{\quad} + \underline{\quad} = 9$ on the board. Ask, Can this number fact be a double fact or double-plus-1 fact? How do you know? What might the missing numbers be? Which numbers cannot be the missing numbers? How do you know?

Repeat the discussion with the incomplete number sentences below.

$$\underline{\quad} + \underline{\quad} = 14 \qquad \underline{\quad} + \underline{\quad} = 31$$

$$\underline{\quad} + \underline{\quad} = 23 \qquad \underline{\quad} + \underline{\quad} = 35$$

$$\underline{\quad} + \underline{\quad} = 26 \qquad \underline{\quad} + \underline{\quad} = 38$$

Double Plus 2

Introduce

1. Make two cube trains as shown below and show them to the students. Ask, What number fact do these show? (Five add seven.) What do you notice about this fact? (It is almost a double.) What facts can you use to help you figure out the total? The students should be able to explain that they can either double 5 and count on 2, or double 7 and count back 2. Some students may know that a cube can be taken off the longer train and added to the shorter one to make double six. Repeat with other double-plus-2 facts.

2. Select or make the double-plus-2 cards shown (the dotted circles indicate what is on the back of the flap). Hold the 5 + 7 card so that the flap with seven dots is folded back on the right-hand side as seen by the students. Ask, What fact do you see? (Double five.) How many dots are there in total? (Ten.) Fold the flap forward so that the seven dots cover five dots. Ask, How many dots are there now? How do you know? Repeat with other cards, including turnarounds.

Fact File

In the operation of addition, the parts that are being added together are called *addends*. The total that they form is called the *sum*.

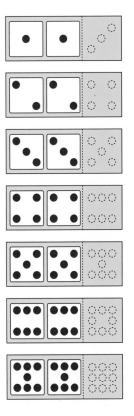

See: *Use-Doubles Strategy Cards*

3. Give each student (or pair of students) twenty-two connecting cubes of two colors (e.g. eleven red and eleven blue). Have the students use their cubes to make a train that shows a double-plus-2 fact as in *Introduce* Activity 1. Have them write the number fact their cubes show and then repeat the activity with another fact.

Reinforce

1 ▸ Have the students write and illustrate some double-plus-2 stories. For example, *Jasmine has five crayons. Pete has seven crayons. How many crayons are there in total?* Invite students to share their stories and then ask the rest of the class to raise their hands if they wrote a story about the same addition fact.

2 ▸ Draw the domino shown below on the board. Ask the students to say the fact they see (4 + 4 = 8) and write this above the domino. Call on two other students to say the two double-plus-2 facts associated with the domino (4 + 6 = 10 and 6 + 4 = 10). Write these facts below the domino. Give each student a copy of Blackline Master 27. Read the instructions with the class. The students can complete the sheets individually.

3 ▸ Write the numerals 1 to 20 on the board. Say, *Choose a number between one and ten. When you double it, what is the total?* As the students identify the doubles, draw a ✓ above each numeral.

✓ ✓ ✓ ✓ ✓ ✓ ✓ ✓ ✓ ✓
1 2 3 4 5 6 7 8 9 10 11 12 13 14 15 16 17 18 19 20

Now ask, *When you double a number and add two, what totals do you get? How do you know?* As the students identify the answers, draw a ✗ below each numeral.

✓ ✓ ✓ ✓ ✓ ✓ ✓ ✓ ✓ ✓
1 2 3 4 5 6 7 8 9 10 11 12 13 14 15 16 17 18 19 20
    ✗ ✗ ✗ ✗ ✗ ✗ ✗ ✗ ✗

Ask the students to describe what they notice. Encourage a variety of observations. For example, double-plus-2 facts and double facts share the same totals and both sets of totals are always even numbers.

Fact File

A *number* is used for counting, labeling, and ordering. The base-ten system uses ten symbols (0, 1, 2, 3, 4, 5, 6, 7, 8, 9) called *digits* to represent numbers.

A *numeral* is a single digit or combination of digits. For example, 36 is a two-digit numeral to represent the number thirty-six.

---

4 ▸ Write ___ + ___ = ___ on the board. Ask, *What is the total for a double-plus-2 fact? What numbers can you add to get that total? How do you know?* Ask one student to give the total and write it on the board. Then ask the other members of the class to say the double-plus-2 fact that matches. Encourage the students to describe the numbers in either order before writing them on the board. For example:

$$6 + 8 = 14$$

$$8 + 6 = 14$$

Repeat as time permits. At a later stage, ask the students to identify double facts which will give the same totals. For example, 16 can be the result of doubling 8 or adding 9 and 7.

5 Select or make a set of double-plus-2 flash cards as shown below (the turnaround fact is on the back of each card). The cards should be made of exactly the same paper as the flash cards used previously. Some of the cards will have been used to teach other facts. Combine these with the cards used in *Practice* Activity 1 on page 35 and *Practice* Activity 1 on page 40. Distribute a card to each student.

0 + 2 = _	1 + 3 = _
2 + 4 = _	3 + 5 = _
4 + 6 = _	5 + 7 = _
6 + 8 = _	7 + 9 = _

See: *Addition Flash Cards*

Fact File

The word *double* comes from the Latin word *duplus*. This is a combination of *duo*, meaning "two", and *plus*, which means "fold". When something is folded over itself there are twice as many layers as before. *Two-fold* is a direct translation still used today. Examples of related words are a *duplex* apartment (a two-storey residence) and *duplicate* (to make two of something).

Copy Blackline Masters 7 and 12 and cut out the numeral cards. Lay them in a column on the floor. Ask the students to raise their hands if they have a double card. Choose one of these students and have them identify and place their card beside the matching numeral card on the floor. For example, a student will place a flash card showing 6 + 6 = ___ beside the numeral card showing 12. Ask, **Who has a card that involves doubling (six) then adding one or two? Where will those cards go? How do you know?** Repeat for other doubles.

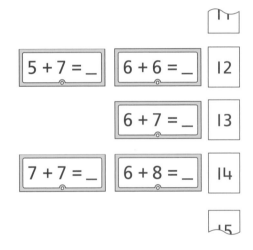

6 Reuse the numeral cards from the previous activity. Select a card at random and ask, **Is this the total for a double-plus-2 fact? How do you know? Is there a double-plus-1 fact that has this total? What count-on fact matches?** Repeat with other cards from the set.

Practice

1 Reuse the double-sided cards from *Reinforce* Activity 5 on page 45. Randomly select a card and show it to the class for approximately three seconds. Have the students write or say the answer. Repeat with other cards from the set.

2 This is a game for two teams. Copy Blackline Masters 7 and 12 and cut out the numeral cards. Provide the students with a complete set of double-nine dominoes and have them find all the dominoes that show double, double-plus-1, and double-plus-2 facts. For example, the three dominoes that involve doubling 4 are shown below. These dominoes will be used for the game.

To play the game:

- The dominoes are placed facedown and mixed around. The teams take turns to pick an equal number of dominoes, keeping them facedown. Any extra dominoes are placed to one side.

- The numeral cards are spread out face up in a line between the two teams.

- At a starting time, the players work quickly to match their dominoes to the numeral cards. Players should ensure their dominoes stay on their team's side of the numeral cards.

- Once both teams are finished, all players check the matching for accuracy. All the correct matches for each team are placed to one side.

- The first team to finish the matching earns five points. Then each team earns one bonus point for each correct match.

- The team with the most points wins.

3 Give each student a copy of Blackline Master 28. Make sure they understand the instructions. The students can complete the sheet individually.

4 This is a game for two players. Each pair will need a set of numeral cards from Blackline Masters 7 and 12, a spinner from Blackline Master 8, and a paper clip. Have the students straighten the paper clip to use with the spinner. Explain to the students that the numeral cards each represent a total for an addition fact.

To play the game:

- The numeral cards are spread out in a row in front of the two players.

- The first player spins the paper clip.

- The player can then double the resulting number, double and add 1, or double and add 2 to make a total that matches one of the numeral cards. The player then removes the matching numeral card from the row and places it to one side.

- The other player has a turn.

- As the game continues, the player misses that turn if no matching numeral cards are available.

- Once all the cards have been claimed, the player who has the greatest number of cards wins.

5 Distribute the students' record sheets used in *Practice* Activity 6 on page 36 (Blackline Master 25). Direct them to fold the sheet so that they can see only the *Double-Plus-2* section. This assessment task should take no more than one minute for the students to complete. A longer period of time may indicate that recall of the facts is not automatic. Collect the sheets afterward and record the results for each student on Blackline Masters 1 and 2. See page 4 of the *Introduction* for instructions.

Extend

1. Write **22** on the board. Ask, What number can you double to get this answer? How do you know? Write **22 = 11 + 11** on the board. Ask, What other facts have the same total? How do you know? Discuss the possibilities and encourage the students to think of any "near doubles" that might help, such as 10 + 12 = 22 and its turnaround 12 + 10 = 22. Repeat with other two-digit numbers.

2. On the board, write the following number sentences:

    20 + 20 = ___

    20 + 21 = ___

    20 + 22 = ___

Ask, What is the total for the first fact? How did you figure it out? How can you use that fact to figure out the totals for the other facts? Repeat with these number sentences:

    21 + 21 = ___

    21 + 22 = ___

    22 + 22 = ___

Repeat with numbers slightly greater than 30 and 40 (for example, 31 and 41).

3. Write these number sentences on the board:

    20 + 19 = ___

    20 + 18 = ___

Ask, What do you know about the size of the totals? How do you know? One possible explanation that the students may offer is, "The totals are less than forty because double twenty is forty." Invite the students to explain how they can figure out the totals for each number sentence. Repeat with other numbers slightly less than 30 and 40 (for example, 29 and 39).

4. Draw the grids shown below on the board or an overhead transparency.

14	14	14
15	15	15
16	16	16

14	14	14
15	15	15
16	16	16

TOTALS

28	29	29
30	30	30
31	31	32

Invite a volunteer to choose a number from the totals grid. Ask, What two numbers in the other grids add together to give this total? How do you know your answer is correct? For example, if a student chooses 29 then they can choose 14 from the first grid on the left and 15 from the middle grid. Cross out the three numbers in the grids. After the volunteer explains their thinking, encourage other members of the class to suggest different thinking strategies for the same three numbers. Continue the activity for other numbers until all the numbers in the grids are crossed out.

Bridge to 10

The bridge-to-ten strategy includes facts that have one addend close to 10. In these instances, 10 can be used as a reference point to help students figure out totals when one part involves 9, 8, or 7. For example, the total of 9 + 6 is the same as 10 + 5.

Fact File

The bridge-to-10 strategy is also known as *bridge the decades*, *bridging across 10*, *bridging through 10*, *making 10*, *make to 10*, and *use 10*.

Prepare

1 Arrange the students into groups and give each group approximately one hundred connecting cubes. The students should try to represent all the different combinations of 10 that they can think of using two different colors (as shown below). Once the groups have finished, invite volunteers to show the combinations.

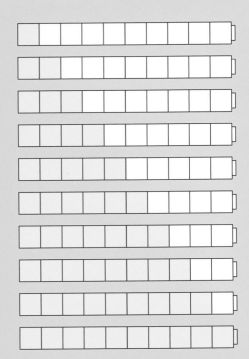

2 This is a game for two players. Give each pair of students a double ten-frame and a bag of mixed counters. Each pair of students will also need a standard six-sided die.

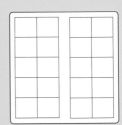

See: *Bridge-to-10 Frames*

To play the game:

- Players sit on opposite sides of the double ten-frame so that they each have a single ten-frame.

- The first player rolls the die and places counters of one color on their ten-frame. They say how many more they need to make 10 then give the die to the other player.

- The other player has a turn.

- The players continue taking turns, using a different color counter for each turn. If a player rolls a number that makes their total number of counters exceed 10, they miss a turn.

- The first player to fill their ten-frame exactly is the winner.

At different stages of the game, check that the students are saying the number required to make 10. As a game finishes, ask the students to describe the sequence of the numbers that they rolled. For example, they may say, "I rolled two first so I needed eight more to make ten. I knew I could not do that because the highest number I can roll is six. Then I rolled four so I needed to roll another four to make ten. I rolled a four and won the game."

Introduce

1 Use counters and a double ten-frame (as shown below) to represent 9 + 4. Ask, **What is the total of nine add four? How do you know?** Ask volunteers to use the counters to show how they figured out the answer. If necessary, move one of the four counters to completely fill the left-hand frame. Ask the students to say the new fact they see (10 + 3 = 13).

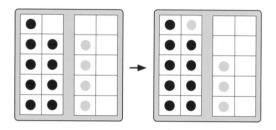

See: *Bridge-to-10 Frames*

Repeat this activity with other facts that involve 9. Invite individuals to move the counters as required. As you show examples of turnarounds (such as 4 + 9 = 13) be sure to highlight how one counter is moved from the lesser number to the greater number so that it is easier to calculate.

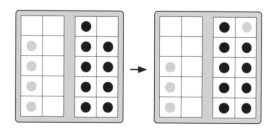

Fact File

Double ten-frames can be used so that the frames are side-by-side or one above the other. Although students should be exposed to both formats, the side-by-side format relates better to the equation and stresses that no formal written method is necessary for these basic facts.

2 On the board or an overhead transparency, draw a number line from 1 to 20 and write **9 + 4 = ___** below. Ask, **What is the total if you add nine and four? How did you figure it out?** Invite volunteers to describe and demonstrate their thinking using the number line. Ensure that the students start from the greater number, without drawing a jump to it. Have the students write the size of each jump (e.g. + 4) above the arrow.

Point to 10 on the number line and ask, **If we start at nine and need to add four, we can jump to ten. How far do we jump to get from nine to ten?** (One.) **So how much further do we have to jump now?** (Three.) Draw the two jumps as shown below and ensure that the students understand that the total of the two jumps is 4.

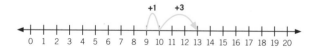

Repeat with other number sentences, such as:

$$8 + 5 = \underline{\quad}$$

$$4 + 7 = \underline{\quad}$$

$$6 + 9 = \underline{\quad}$$

$$5 + 8 = \underline{\quad}$$

3 Give each student a double ten-frame and twenty counters in two different colors (for example, ten red and ten blue). Repeat *Introduce* Activity 1 on page 50, with each student using their own double ten-frame to demonstrate the facts. When the students are comfortable with showing facts involving 9, work through problems involving 8 and then 7.

Some students may use count-on facts or double facts to help them initially. In such cases, invite them to share their thinking with the rest of the class and discuss the different ways an unknown total can be figured out. It is better for students to have an understanding of how different strategies can be used to figure out the same addition fact, rather than have them rigidly stick to only one method.

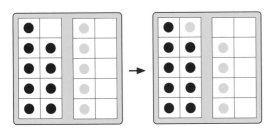

9 + 5   is the same as   10 + 4

To introduce bridging to 10 in a slightly different way, use *Bridge-to-10 Strategy Cards*.

4 The other strategies covered in this book have names that are easily identified with the process that is involved, such as the count-on-1 and double-plus-2 strategies. The bridge-to-10 strategy is slightly more abstract and some students may benefit from pictures or models linking the strategy to actual bridges. For example, join two trains of ten connecting cubes and lay them side by side with a gap in between. Place nine craft sticks on the cube trains to create a "bridge" as shown. Place a number of craft sticks beside the "bridge". Revisit some of the previous activities using the craft sticks to bridge to 10.

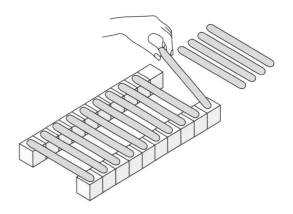

Fact File

The term *bridging* is also used to describe operating across two adjacent place values. For example, 15 + 8 involves bridging because the total of the ones affects the total of the tens.

Reinforce

1 Have the students write and illustrate some addition stories that involve 7, 8, or 9. For example, *Natasha has nine jelly beans. I give her four more. How many jelly beans does she have now?* Invite individual students to share their stories and then ask whether anyone else had a story that used the same addition fact or its turnaround.

2 Give each student a copy of Blackline Master 29. Make sure they understand how to complete the sheet then have them work individually. When finished, discuss each question and ask, *What is another way to figure out this fact?*

3 Write 9 + ___ = ___ on the board. Ask, *If the total is less than twenty, what might the other missing number be? How do you know?* Encourage the students to say all of the possible solutions and to explain their thinking. As they suggest solutions, write each number sentence on the board. In this way, members of the class can use the information for one number sentence to help them create another sentence. For example, a student might make a new sentence by seeing 9 + 7 = 16 and thinking, "If I add one to seven the total will be one more than sixteen. So nine add eight is seventeen."

Repeat the activity using 8 + ___ = ___.

4 Write 17 = ___ + ___ on the board. Ask, *What numbers make this sentence true? How do you know?* Encourage the students to say all of the possible solutions. Write the sentences on the board as the students explain their thinking (all of the possible solutions are shown below, without their turnarounds). Discuss how adding 1 to an addend means that 1 must be subtracted from the other addend to achieve the same total. Encourage the students to use their own words to explain this idea.

$$17 = 17 + 0 \quad\quad 17 = 16 + 1$$
$$17 = 15 + 2 \quad\quad 17 = 14 + 3$$
$$17 = 13 + 4 \quad\quad 17 = 12 + 5$$
$$17 = 11 + 6 \quad\quad 17 = 10 + 7$$
$$17 = 9 + 8$$

Once all possible number sentences (and their turnarounds) have been written ask, *What patterns do you see? Which facts are easy to remember? Why?* Discuss the students' ideas and then ask, *Which number sentences have one or both addends close to ten?* Loop the sentences that the students suggest (including turnarounds). The number sentences they suggest could vary, but generally sentences with addends equal to 12, 11, 10, 9, and 8 should be looped.

Repeat the activity for other number sentences with answers ranging from 13 to 19.

Practice

1 ▶ Select or make the double-sided bridge-to-10 flash cards shown below (the turnaround fact is on the back of each card). The cards should be made of exactly the same paper as the other flash cards used previously. Show one card and invite a student to say the answer. Allow approximately three seconds for the student to provide the answer. Repeat several times with other students and cards.

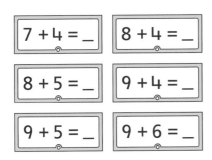

7 + 4 = _	8 + 4 = _
8 + 5 = _	9 + 4 = _
9 + 5 = _	9 + 6 = _

See: *Addition Flash Cards*

2 ▶ Give each pair of students two blank cubes. Instruct them to write the numerals 9, 9, 8, 8, 7, and 7 on one cube and 4, 4, 5, 5, 6, and 6 on the other cube. Each 6 and 9 should be underlined to avoid confusion. Each pair of students rolls the cubes and records the matching bridge-to-10 fact. Students may choose to record more than one fact. Repeat as time allows.

3 ▶ This is a game for two players. Each player will need four counters (a different color for each student). Give each pair a copy of Blackline Master 24 and reuse the cubes from the previous activity. Draw the grid shown on the board and direct one student in each pair to copy it onto the top half of their grid.

11	14	13
15	12	15
11	15	13
12	14	11

To play the game:

- The first player rolls both cubes.

- The player then adds the numerals rolled and covers the total on the grid with one of their counters.

- The other player has a turn.

- As the game continues, the player misses a turn if the total has already been covered.

- The first player to place all four counters on the grid wins.

As the students play the game, ask questions such as, **What do you need to roll to place a counter on that total?**

4 ▶ Give each student a copy of Blackline Master 30. Read the instructions and then direct them to complete the sheet individually.

5 ▶ Distribute the students' record sheets used in *Practice* Activity 6 on page 36 (Blackline Master 25). Direct them to fold the sheet so that they can see only the *Bridge-to-10* section. This assessment task should take no more than about $1\frac{1}{2}$ minutes for the students to complete. A longer period of time may indicate that recall of the facts is not automatic. Collect the sheets afterward and record the results for each student on Blackline Masters 1 and 2. See page 4 of the *Introduction* for instructions.

Extend

1 Write these number sentences on the board:

9 + 5 = ___

19 + 5 = ___

29 + 5 = ___

39 + 5 = ___

Point to the first number sentence and ask, What is this answer? How can you use it to figure out the other answers? Encourage the students to use patterns to explain their thinking. Repeat the activity with similar sequences beginning with 9 or 8.

2 Write 9 + ___ = ___ on the board. Ask, What number can you add to nine to get an answer that is more than twenty? What is the answer? How do you know? Encourage the students to begin by using numbers that are easy for them to add. For example, 9 + 20 = ___, 9 + 30 = ___, and 9 + 50 = ___. After several numbers have been suggested, encourage all members of the class to explain different strategies for checking the answer. Repeat the discussion using 8 + ___ = ___.

3 Write the following number sentences on the board:

9 + 5 = ___

9 + 15 = ___

9 + 25 = ___

9 + 35 = ___

Ask, What totals do you know? How do you know them? When all of the number sentences have been completed ask, What patterns do you notice?

Beside the first set of number sentences, write:

9 + 6 = ___

9 + 16 = ___

9 + 26 = ___

9 + 36 = ___

Ask, Which missing totals do you know? How can you figure out the answers that you do not know? Encourage the students to explain a range of strategies. Repeat the activity using 9 and other number sequences. The entire activity can be repeated using 8 as the first addend.

4 Discuss adding two numbers that are close to a multiple of 10 (for example, 19 and 29). Ask, How can you figure out the total of these two numbers? Discuss the methods the students use. Invite volunteers to suggest other number sentences they can add in the same way.

5 Draw the number line shown below on the board or on an overhead transparency. Ask, What number could be at the start of the jump? (Twenty-nine.) If it is twenty-nine, what number will be at the end of the jump? How do you know? (Twenty-nine add four is thirty-three because nine add four is thirteen.) Redraw the "jump" arrow in a different position and repeat.

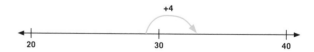

All the Facts

The activities in this section are designed to help students revisit their knowledge of all the basic addition facts and the count-on, use-doubles, and bridge-to-10 strategies. Therefore, the activities begin with reinforcing what the students know. Compile a complete set of addition flash cards from the following activities:

Reinforce Activity 3, page 13
Practice Activity 1, page 18
Reinforce Activity 4, page 23
Reinforce Activity 2, page 28
Practice Activity 1, page 35
Practice Activity 1, page 40
Reinforce Activity 5, page 45
Practice Activity 1, page 53

Reinforce

1 Review the students' tracking sheets and facts grids that have been used to record the facts the students know. If most students know all the basic facts, ask them during class time to write five facts that they find the easiest and five facts they find the most difficult. This will give some indication of which activities in the book need to be revisited.

2 Give each student a copy of Blackline Master 31. Read the stories with the class then have the students complete the sheet individually.

3 Have the students write their own number stories to match given number facts. Use number facts from a range of addition strategies, for example:

$$9 + 6 = 15$$

$$3 + 4 = 7$$

$$7 + 2 = 9$$

Then have the students write number stories to give to a partner to solve. Their partner can also write the matching number fact.

4 Copy Blackline Masters 7 and 12 and cut out the numeral cards. Make an additional card for 0. Place the cards in a column on the floor. Give each student two or three addition flash cards. The students can then take turns to place a card beside the matching numeral card. As the cards are being placed ask the students what they notice. They should observe that some totals (such as 0, 1, 2, 16, 17, and 18) have very few facts that match, while others (such as 8, 9, and 10) have many. When the activity is complete, ask questions such as,

Which numbers have the most (or least) facts? Starting at zero, what happens to the number of facts for each total? (They increase up to nine then they decrease.) Look at eighteen. Is nine add nine the only way to make eighteen? What other way could you do it? Discuss the students' thinking strategies and allow them to describe anything else they notice.

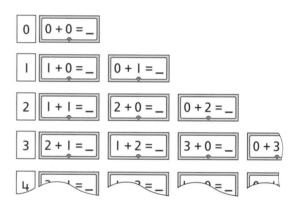

5 Write the numerals 0 to 7 on the board. Ask, Which two numbers can we add to make seven? As the students suggest combinations, draw a curved line to connect the numbers to make a number-fact rainbow as shown below. Repeat for other odd numbers less than 10.

Write the numerals from 0 to 6 on the board and repeat the question. Draw curved lines to connect the combinations and note how the numeral 3 has an arc that joins up to itself. Repeat for other even numbers less than 10.

Direct the students to create number-fact rainbows for all the numbers from 1 to 10 (including 1 and 10). Then have the students select three numbers less than 20 and create number-fact rainbows for them. Discuss the students' results and highlight that the greater a number is, the more combinations it has. Highlight that all the even-number totals involve a double.

Fact File

Creating a number-fact rainbow for zero is one way of demonstrating that it is an even number.

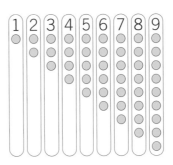

6 It will be useful for the students to review the strategies that they can use for different facts. Copy the table shown and complete it with the students. Encourage discussion of facts that involve more than one strategy. Some students may have a preference for one strategy over another, while some students may use an entirely different strategy to figure out the fact.

	Strategy		
Fact	Count on	Use doubles	Bridge to 10
3 + 4 = 7	Yes	Yes	No
8 + 5 = 13			
4 + 4 = 8			
3 + 9 = 12			
6 + 7 = 13			
5 + 2 = 7			

7 The students can work in groups for this activity. Give each group a set of the craft sticks shown below. Ask each group to show the stick with eight dots. Ask, Is there another way we can show eight dots? Encourage the students to see that they can use a combination of two sticks to show eight dots. Some may see that they can use more than two sticks (such as combining 1, 3, and 4) but restrict the activity to using two sticks at this stage. Invite volunteers from each group to show different combinations of 8. Repeat the discussion with other numbers.

At a later time, extend the activity by asking questions such as, How can we show fourteen using two sticks? Three sticks? Four sticks? Repeat the discussion using other "teen" numbers.

Practice

1 This is a game for three or four players. Give each group a set of all the addition flash cards. Instruct them to group all the cards together, shuffle them, and then place them facedown in the middle.

To play the game:

- Players take turns selecting a flash card.

- As a player has three cards that have the same total, these are grouped and placed in front of the player.

- As a player picks up a card that has the same answer as one of their existing groups, then that card can also be added to the group in front of them.

- Play continues until no more cards remain in the middle. The player who has the greatest number of cards grouped in front of them wins.

2 This is a game for two or more teams of at least five students. Use chalk to draw a large 3-by-4 grid on the pavement or floor. Write the numerals 0 to 11 in the spaces of the grid. You will also need two small beanbags. Direct the teams to stand in lines about six steps away from the grid.

To play the game:

- The first player in one team throws the two beanbags onto the grid and adds the two numbers.

- The first player in the other team repeats the process.

- The team with the greatest total earns one point.

- The first players from each team move to the back of their respective lines.

- The process is repeated with the next player from each team.

- The game finishes when each player has had one or two turns. The team with the greatest number of points wins.

The rules can be varied so that the aim is to score the least number of points. Points can also be allocated to the team that scores the lowest total in each round.

3 This is a game for two players. Give each student a copy of Blackline Master 32 and each pair a blank cube. Have the students write 4, 5, 6, 7, 8, and 9 on the faces of the cube. Ensure they underline the 6 and 9 to avoid confusion. Read the instructions to the students.

To play the game:

- The first player rolls the cube.

- Both players write the number in the middle of the first target. They then add the number to each of the numbers shown on the target and write the totals in the outer ring.

- The players race each other to complete all the facts in the target accurately.

- After each target is completed the students check their answers and write their scores (one point for each correct total).

- The second player rolls the cube and the process is repeated.

- Play continues in this way until all the targets are completed.

- Each player calculates their own total score. The player with the greatest total score wins.

Extend

1 Write **7 + 6 = ___** on the board. Ask, *If you change the seven to eight, how will the answer change? How do you know?* Write the new number sentence, **8 + 6 = ___**, on the board.

Encourage the students to explain why the answer for this sentence must be one more than the first sentence. For example, they may say, "Eight is one more than seven and the second number is the same in both sentences, so the total must be one more." They can use connecting cubes to help demonstrate their thinking. Repeat the discussion by asking the students to change one of the numbers in each new sentence. Write the new sentences on the board (some possible sentences are shown below). After seven or eight sentences have been suggested, ask the students to say the total for each number sentence. Write the answers on the board. If the students are not sure about any of the answers, encourage them to use the total of the previous sentence to help.

$$7 + 6 = \_\_\_$$

$$8 + 6 = \_\_\_$$

$$8 + 7 = \_\_\_$$

$$10 + 7 = \_\_\_$$

$$12 + 7 = \_\_\_$$

$$12 + 9 = \_\_\_$$

$$12 + 11 = \_\_\_$$

2 Number boards can be used to initiate many activities and discussions for addition. Make an overhead transparency of Blackline Master 33. Draw a loop around 34 and ask, *What number is two more than thirty-four? Twelve more than thirty-four? Twenty-two more? Thirty-two more? How do you know?* Invite students to loop each numeral and explain the pattern they see. Repeat this discussion, starting with other addends. For example, start with 14 and add 3, 13, 23, and so on.

3 Use the number board transparency again to discuss ways of adding numbers that are a little less than a multiple of 10. For example, loop 35 and invite a volunteer to show how they would add 9 more. Ask, *How did you know the answer?* The discussion will vary, but the student might say, "I added ten first, then I subtracted one." Encourage the class to suggest other ways that they can add 9. For example, adding 9 is the same as subtracting 1 then adding 10. Repeat this discussion with other addends. For example, start with 44 and add 9, 19, 29, 39, and so on.

4 Draw pieces of a number board on the board (as shown below). Have the students say the numbers that will be the other end of each piece. Make sure they explain how they know their numbers are correct.

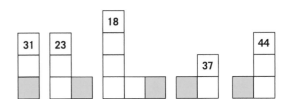

Facts Grid

Name: _____

Find the first addend in the left-hand column. Then find the second addend in the top row.

+	0	1	2	3	4	5	6	7	8	9
0	0	1	2	3	4	5	6	7	8	9
1	1	2	3	4	5	6	7	8	9	10
2	2	3	4	5	6	7	8	9	10	11
3	3	4	5	6	7	8	9	10	11	12
4	4	5	6	7	8	9	10	11	12	13
5	5	6	7	8	9	10	11	12	13	14
6	6	7	8	9	10	11	12	13	14	15
7	7	8	9	10	11	12	13	14	15	16
8	8	9	10	11	12	13	14	15	16	17
9	9	10	11	12	13	14	15	16	17	18

Student Tracking Chart

	Student Names	Count on 1	Count on 2	Count on 3	Count on 0	Double	Double plus 1	Double plus 2	Bridge to 10
1									
2									
3									
4									
5									
6									
7									
8									
9									
10									
11									
12									
13									
14									
15									
16									
17									
18									
19									
20									
21									
22									
23									
24									
25									
26									
27									
28									
29									
30									

Domino Arrangement

Groups of Two Arrangement

Groups of Three Arrangement

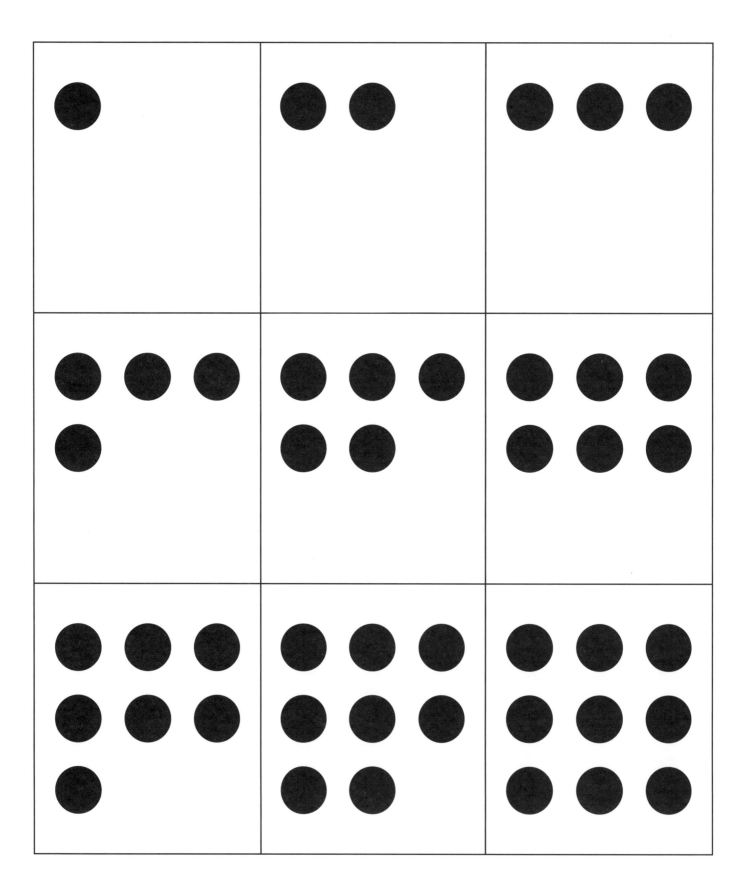

Count-on Challenge

Name: _____

Draw the dots. Count on. Write the new numbers.

a.	b.	c. 6
d. 2	e. 5	f.
g.	h. 8	i.
j.	k.	l. 3
m. 9	n.	o. 7

Numeral Cards 1 to 9

1	2	3
4	5	<u>6</u>
7	8	<u>9</u>

Numbered Spinners

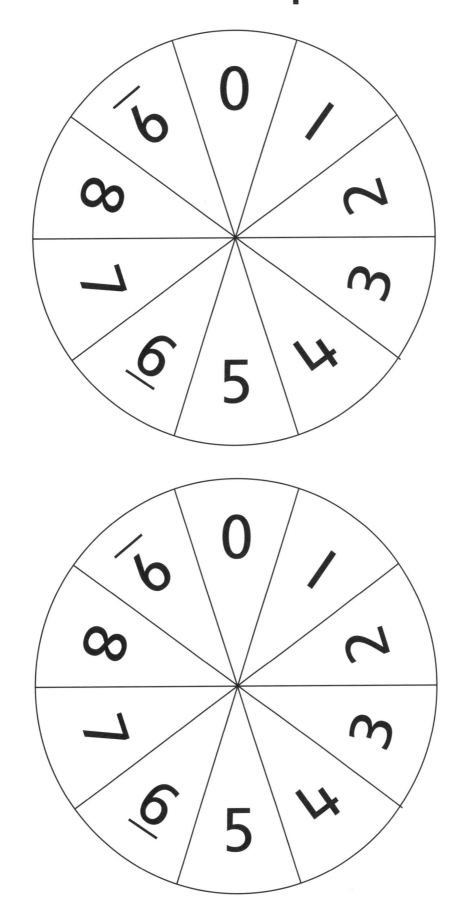

Total Bingo

2	7	2	6	8
5	3	8	3	7
9	6	4	9	4
8	10	7	5	10
5	4	9	8	6

Count-on Bingo

1 + 1	7 + 1	4 + 1	1 + 7	9 + 1
1 + 5	6 + 1	9 + 1	1 + 6	3 + 1
1 + 3	2 + 1	1 + 8	5 + 1	1 + 4
5 + 1	1 + 9	7 + 1	1 + 4	2 + 1
8 + 1	1 + 2	1 + 6	3 + 1	1 + 8

Super Spokes

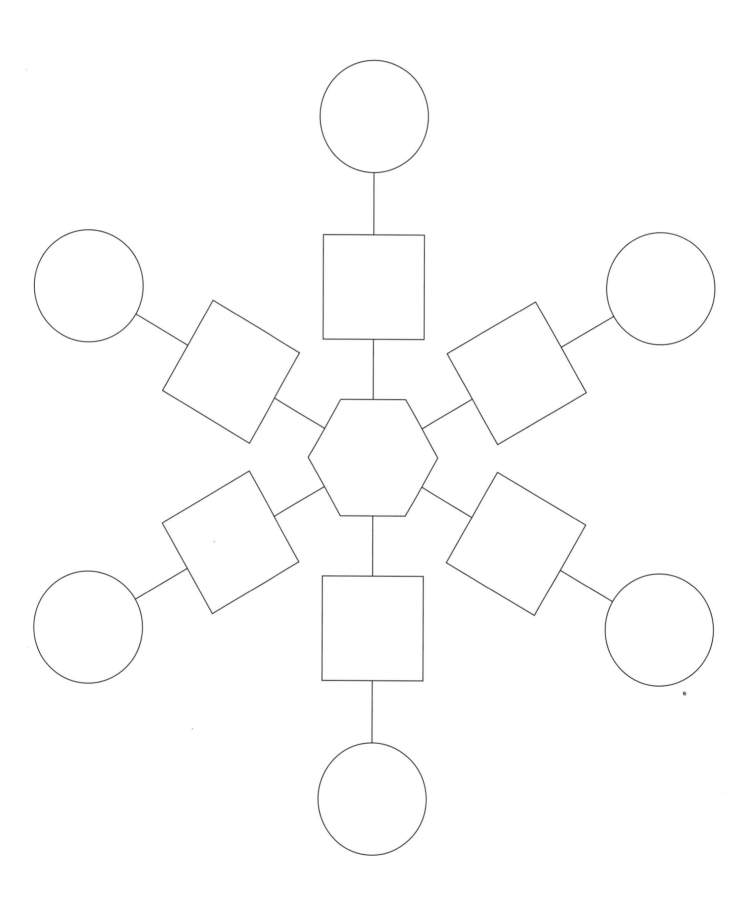

Numeral Cards 10 to 18

10	11	12
13	14	15
<u>1</u>6	17	<u>1</u>8

All Aboard

Complete each number fact.

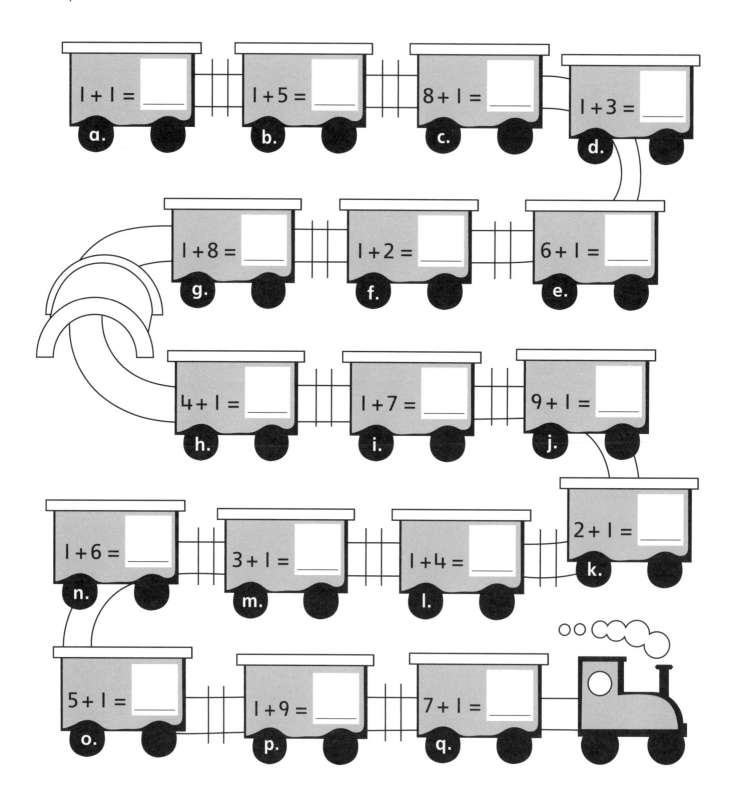

1 + 1 = _____   a.

1 + 5 = _____   b.

8 + 1 = _____   c.

1 + 3 = _____   d.

1 + 8 = _____   g.

1 + 2 = _____   f.

6 + 1 = _____   e.

4 + 1 = _____   h.

1 + 7 = _____   i.

9 + 1 = _____   j.

1 + 6 = _____   n.

3 + 1 = _____   m.

1 + 4 = _____   l.

2 + 1 = _____   k.

5 + 1 = _____   o.

1 + 9 = _____   p.

7 + 1 = _____   q.

Name: _____

Count on 1

Write the answers as fast as you can.

5 + 1 = ____   4 + 1 = ____   1 + 2 = ____

2 + 1 = ____   1 + 1 = ____   7 + 1 = ____

1 + 8 = ____   1 + 7 = ____   1 + 5 = ____

6 + 1 = ____   3 + 1 = ____   8 + 1 = ____

1 + 3 = ____   1 + 4 = ____   1 + 6 = ____

9 + 1 = ____   1 + 9 = ____

Count on 2

Write the answers as fast as you can.

4 + 2 = ____   9 + 2 = ____   6 + 2 = ____

2 + 6 = ____   2 + 2 = ____   2 + 8 = ____

8 + 2 = ____   2 + 3 = ____   5 + 2 = ____

3 + 2 = ____   7 + 2 = ____

2 + 5 = ____   2 + 4 = ____

2 + 7 = ____   2 + 9 = ____

Count on 3

Write the answers as fast as you can.

3 + 3 = ____   4 + 3 = ____

5 + 3 = ____   3 + 6 = ____

3 + 7 = ____   8 + 3 = ____

9 + 3 = ____   3 + 5 = ____

3 + 4 = ____   3 + 9 = ____

6 + 3 = ____   7 + 3 = ____

3 + 8 = ____

Count on 0

Write the answers as fast as you can.

5 + 0 = ____   0 + 1 = ____   2 + 0 = ____

0 + 2 = ____   0 + 5 = ____   0 + 0 = ____

8 + 0 = ____   0 + 8 = ____   0 + 7 = ____

4 + 0 = ____   7 + 0 = ____   6 + 0 = ____

0 + 6 = ____   1 + 0 = ____   0 + 4 = ____

0 + 9 = ____   9 + 0 = ____

3 + 0 = ____   0 + 3 = ____

Knock 'em Down

Name: _____

Complete each number fact.

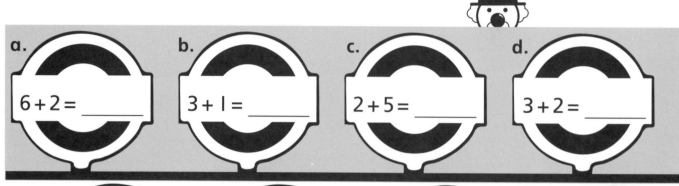

a. 6 + 2 = _____

b. 3 + 1 = _____

c. 2 + 5 = _____

d. 3 + 2 = _____

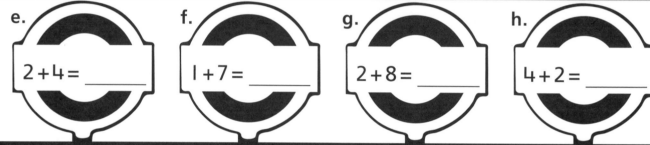

e. 2 + 4 = _____

f. 1 + 7 = _____

g. 2 + 8 = _____

h. 4 + 2 = _____

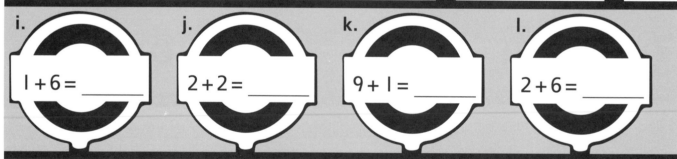

i. 1 + 6 = _____

j. 2 + 2 = _____

k. 9 + 1 = _____

l. 2 + 6 = _____

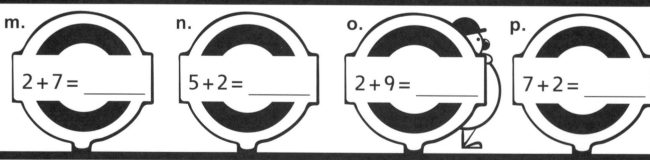

m. 2 + 7 = _____

n. 5 + 2 = _____

o. 2 + 9 = _____

p. 7 + 2 = _____

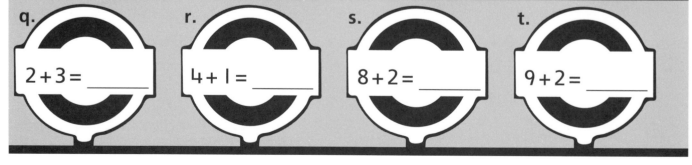

q. 2 + 3 = _____

r. 4 + 1 = _____

s. 8 + 2 = _____

t. 9 + 2 = _____

Count-on Ice Cream

Name: _____

Complete each number fact. Shade matching totals the same.

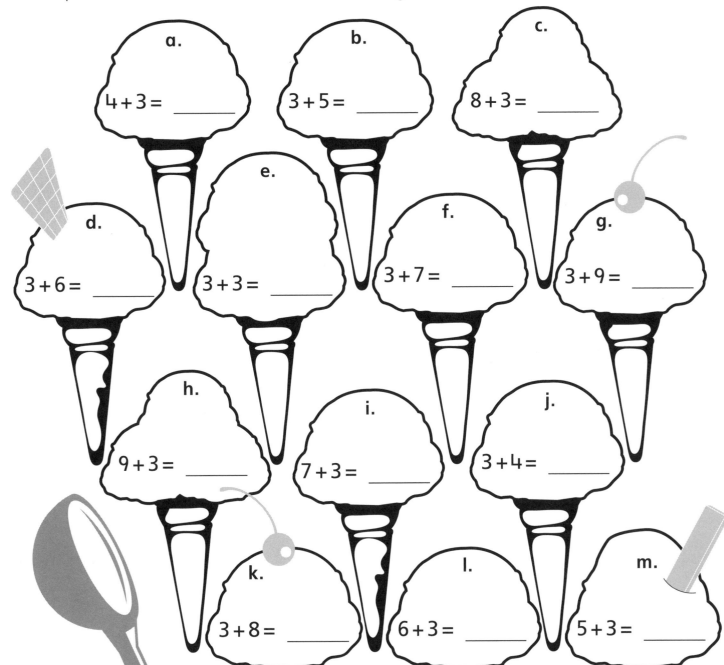

a. 4 + 3 = _____

b. 3 + 5 = _____

c. 8 + 3 = _____

d. 3 + 6 = _____

e. 3 + 3 = _____

f. 3 + 7 = _____

g. 3 + 9 = _____

h. 9 + 3 = _____

i. 7 + 3 = _____

j. 3 + 4 = _____

k. 3 + 8 = _____

l. 6 + 3 = _____

m. 5 + 3 = _____

Test Your Strength

Name: _____

Roll your cubes and count on. Then find your total on a bell and write the matching number fact below.

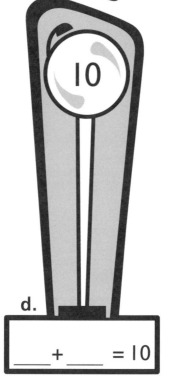

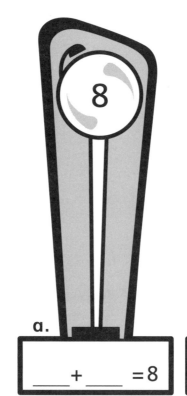
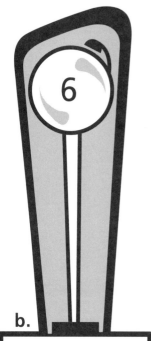
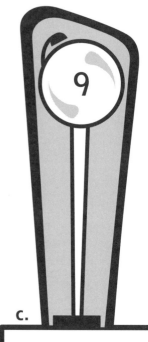

a.

___ + ___ = 8

b.

___ + ___ = 6

c.

___ + ___ = 9

d.

___ + ___ = 10

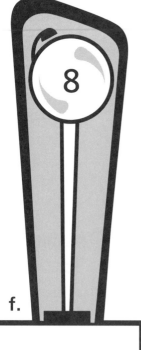
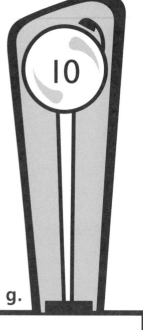

e.

___ + ___ = 7

f.

___ + ___ = 8

g.

___ + ___ = 10

h.

___ + ___ = 11

Diwing Towers

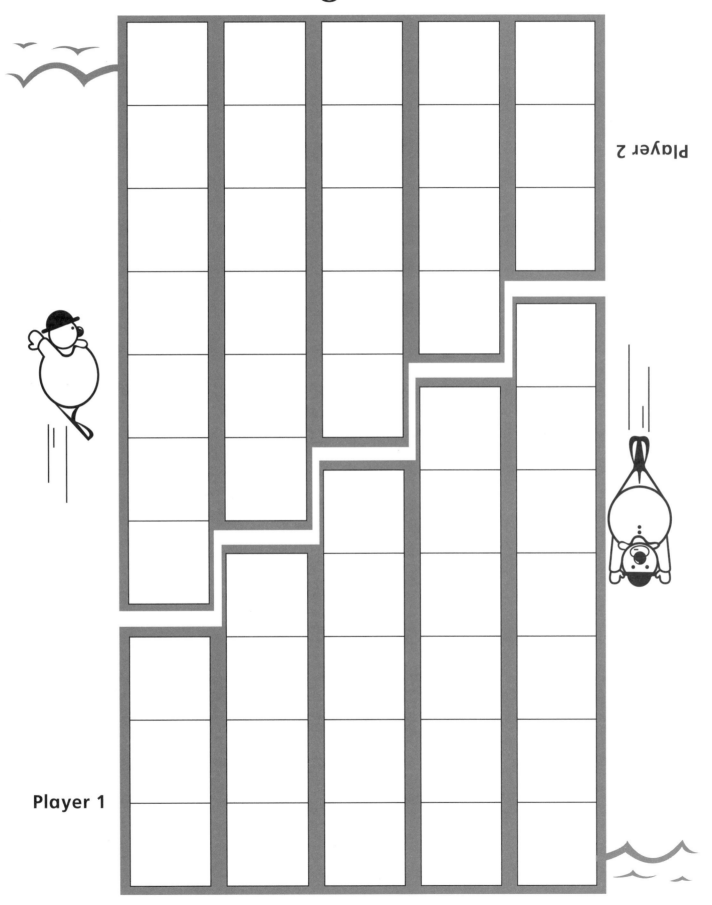

Player 2

Player 1

Count-on Clown

Name: _____

Complete each number fact.

a. 7 + 0 = _____   b. 2 + 0 = _____   c. 5 + 3 = _____

d. 0 + 3 = _____   e. 0 + 6 = _____   f. 8 + 0 = _____

g. 3 + 7 = _____   h. 6 + 3 = _____   i. 0 + 5 = _____

j. 1 + 0 = _____   k. 3 + 9 = _____   l. 8 + 3 = _____

m. 4 + 0 = _____   n. 9 + 3 = _____   o. 0 + 0 = _____

p. 4 + 3 = _____   q. 0 + 9 = _____   r. 3 + 8 = _____

Count-on Wheels

Name: _____

For each of these, shade one number on the wheel and count on 0, 1, 2, and 3.
Write four number facts.

a.

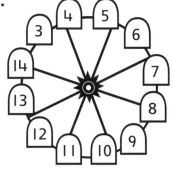

_____ + 0 = _____

_____ + 1 = _____

_____ + 2 = _____

_____ + 3 = _____

b.

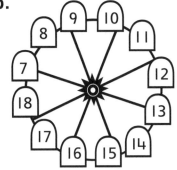

0 + _____ = _____

1 + _____ = _____

2 + _____ = _____

3 + _____ = _____

c.

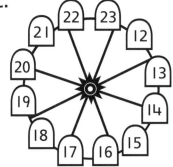

_____ + 0 = _____

_____ + 1 = _____

_____ + 2 = _____

_____ + 3 = _____

d.

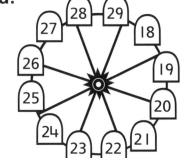

0 + _____ = _____

1 + _____ = _____

2 + _____ = _____

3 + _____ = _____

e.

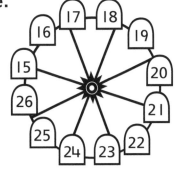

_____ + 0 = _____

_____ + 1 = _____

_____ + 2 = _____

_____ + 3 = _____

f.

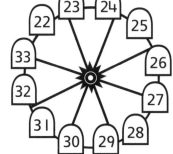

0 + _____ = _____

1 + _____ = _____

2 + _____ = _____

3 + _____ = _____

Drawing Doubles

Name: _____

1. Draw the missing parts to show a double fact. Then write the fact.

a. Draw another hand. 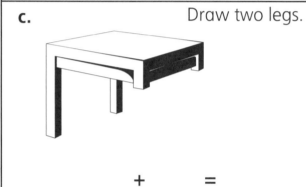 ____ + ____ = ____	**b.** Draw another week. 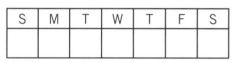 ____ + ____ = ____
c. Draw two legs. ____ + ____ = ____	**d.** Draw four legs.  ____ + ____ = ____

2. Draw dots on the dominoes to show a double fact. Then write the fact.

a. 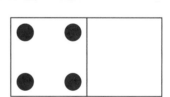 ____ + ____ = ____	**b.** 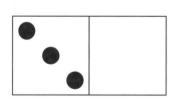 ____ + ____ = ____
c. 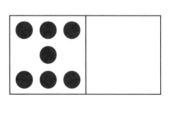 ____ + ____ = ____	**d.** 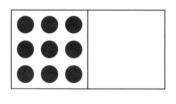 ____ + ____ = ____

Fishing for Facts

Name: _____

Complete each number fact. Then shade the double facts.

a. $5 + 5 =$ _____

b. $1 + 1 =$ _____

c. $8 + 8 =$ _____

d. $4 + 2 =$ _____

e. $6 + 1 =$ _____

f. $2 + 2 =$ _____

g. $3 + 3 =$ _____

h. $3 + 5 =$ _____

i. $5 + 2 =$ _____

j. $6 + 6 =$ _____

k. $9 + 9 =$ _____

l. $4 + 4 =$ _____

m. $7 + 7 =$ _____

n. $3 + 7 =$ _____

o. $2 + 3 =$ _____

Doubles Bingo

3 + 3	8 + 8	1 + 1	9 + 9	5 + 5
5 + 5	4 + 4	7 + 7	6 + 6	7 + 7
9 + 9	6 + 6	0 + 0	8 + 8	0 + 0
3 + 3	7 + 7	9 + 9	1 + 1	4 + 4
8 + 8	5 + 5	2 + 2	6 + 6	2 + 2

Grid

Double

Write the answers as fast as you can.

$4 + 4 =$ _____

$7 + 7 =$ _____

$5 + 5 =$ _____

$9 + 9 =$ _____

$6 + 6 =$ _____

$8 + 8 =$ _____

Double plus 1

Write the answers as fast as you can.

$5 + 6 =$ _____ $\qquad$ $6 + 7 =$ _____

$5 + 4 =$ _____ $\qquad$ $6 + 5 =$ _____

$8 + 7 =$ _____ $\qquad$ $9 + 8 =$ _____

$7 + 6 =$ _____ $\qquad$ $4 + 5 =$ _____

$8 + 9 =$ _____ $\qquad$ $7 + 8 =$ _____

Double plus 2

Write the answers as fast as you can.

$4 + 6 =$ _____ $\qquad$ $6 + 8 =$ _____

$8 + 6 =$ _____ $\qquad$ $7 + 5 =$ _____

$7 + 9 =$ _____ $\qquad$ $9 + 7 =$ _____

$5 + 7 =$ _____

$6 + 4 =$ _____

Bridge to 10

Write the answers as fast as you can.

$9 + 5 =$ _____ $\qquad$ $4 + 7 =$ _____

$4 + 8 =$ _____ $\qquad$ $4 + 9 =$ _____

$9 + 4 =$ _____ $\qquad$ $9 + 6 =$ _____

$7 + 4 =$ _____ $\qquad$ $5 + 9 =$ _____

$6 + 9 =$ _____ $\qquad$ $5 + 8 =$ _____

$8 + 5 =$ _____ $\qquad$ $8 + 4 =$ _____

Balloons

Name: _____

Complete each number fact.
Then shade the totals that are even numbers.

a. $6+7=$ _____

b. $6+5=$ _____

c. $4+3=$ _____

d. $6+6=$ _____

e. $7+8=$ _____

f. $7+6=$ _____

g. $8+7=$ _____

h. $9+8=$ _____

i. $5+6=$ _____

j. $5+4=$ _____

k. $4+5=$ _____

l. $7+7=$ _____

m. $8+9=$ _____

Double Up

Name: _____

For each domino picture
- Write the double fact you see.
- Draw two more dots on one side and write the two new facts you see.

a.

4 + 4 = _____

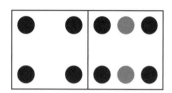

_____ + _____ = _____

_____ + _____ = _____

b.

_____ + _____ = _____

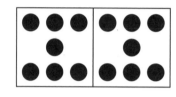

_____ + _____ = _____

_____ + _____ = _____

c.

_____ + _____ = _____

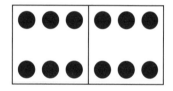

_____ + _____ = _____

_____ + _____ = _____

d.

_____ + _____ = _____

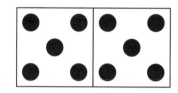

_____ + _____ = _____

_____ + _____ = _____

e.

_____ + _____ = _____

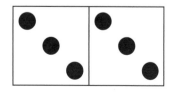

_____ + _____ = _____

_____ + _____ = _____

f.

_____ + _____ = _____

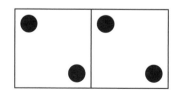

_____ + _____ = _____

_____ + _____ = _____

Clowning Around

Name: _____

These clowns and cars are mixed up. Complete each number fact.
Use a different pencil to shade each set of matching totals.

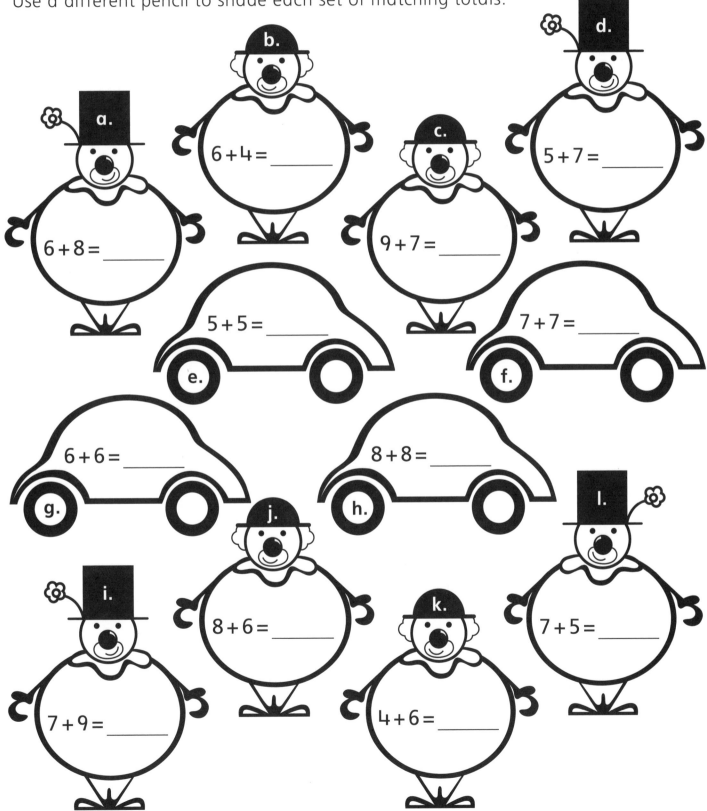

a. 6 + 8 = _____

b. 6 + 4 = _____

c. 9 + 7 = _____

d. 5 + 7 = _____

e. 5 + 5 = _____

f. 7 + 7 = _____

g. 6 + 6 = _____

h. 8 + 8 = _____

i. 7 + 9 = _____

j. 8 + 6 = _____

k. 4 + 6 = _____

l. 7 + 5 = _____

Building Bridges

Name: _____

Draw counters to show the new fact that will help you complete the number fact. Write the missing numbers.

a.

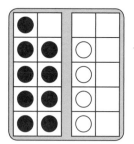

9 + 4 = _____ = 10 + 3

b.

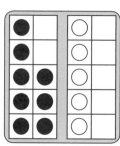

8 + 5 = _____ = 10 + _____

c.

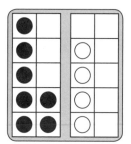

7 + 4 = _____ = 10 + _____

d.

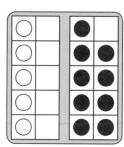
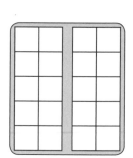

5 + 9 = _____ = 10 + _____

e.

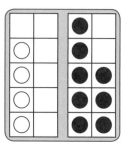

4 + 8 = _____ = 10 + _____

f.

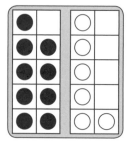
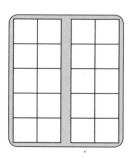

9 + 6 = _____ = 10 + _____

Addition Castle

Name: _____

Complete each number fact. Shade matching totals the same.

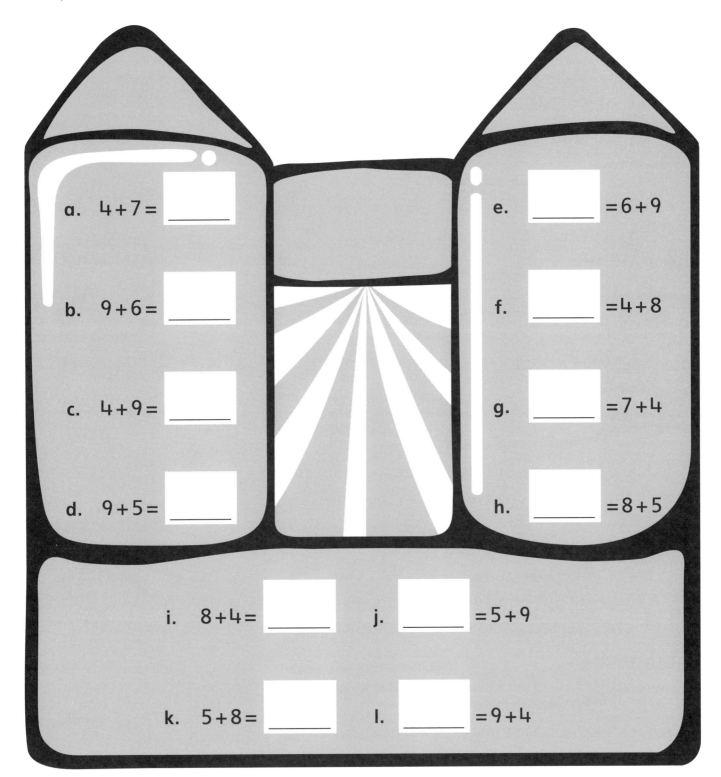

a.   4+7 = _____

b.   9+6 = _____

c.   4+9 = _____

d.   9+5 = _____

e.   _____ = 6+9

f.   _____ = 4+8

g.   _____ = 7+4

h.   _____ = 8+5

i.   8+4 = _____   j.   _____ = 5+9

k.   5+8 = _____   l.   _____ = 9+4

Several Stories

Name: _____

Draw lines to connect each story to its matching number fact. Then write the totals.

a. My family has 2 cats and 4 birds. How many animals do we have in total?

b. There are 5 red apples and 6 green apples in a bowl. How many apples in total?

c. Pam has 7 balloons and Matt has 9 balloons. How many balloons are there in total?

d. Eight birds are sitting on a fence. Another 6 fly down to join them. How many birds are on the fence now?

e. A spider caught 4 flies and 7 moths in its web. How many insects were caught in total?

f. A school has 2 sports teams with 9 players each. How many players are there in total?

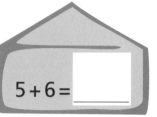

$5+6=$ _____

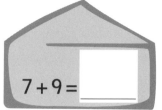

$8+6=$ _____

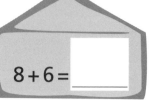

$2+4=$ _____

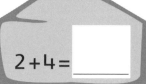

$9+9=$ _____

$7+9=$ _____

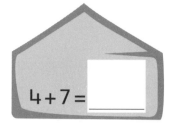

$4+7=$ _____

On Target

Name: _____

For each target, roll your cube and write the number in the middle.
Then write the totals around the outside.

a.

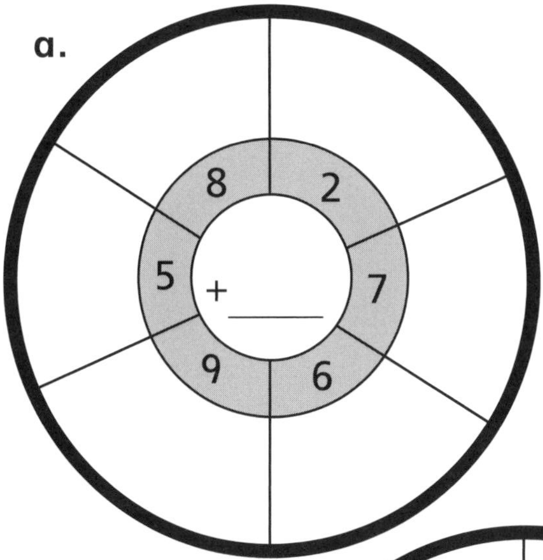

8 2
5 +___ 7
9 6

b.

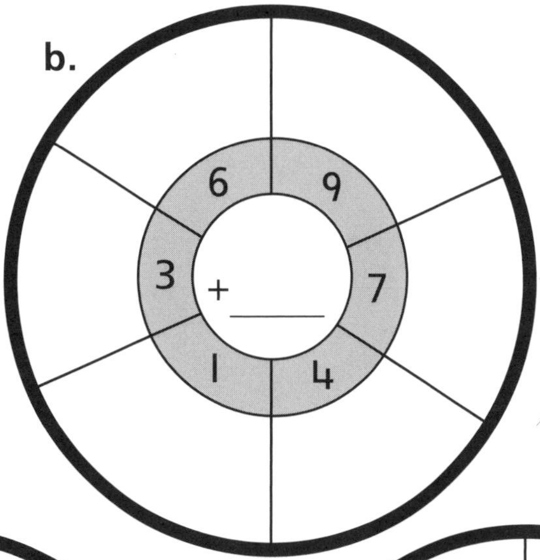

6 9
3 +___ 7
1 4

c.

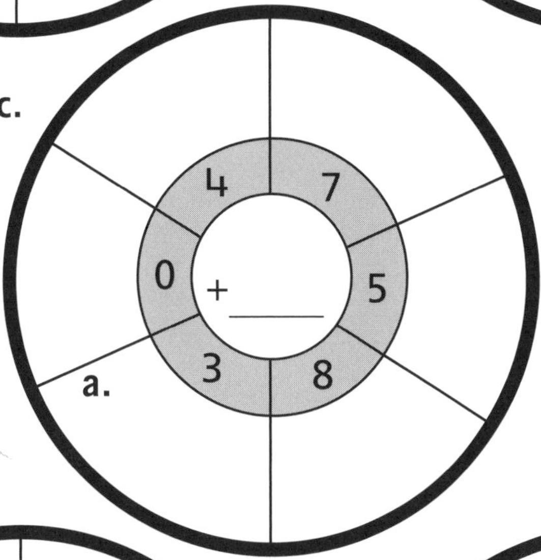

4 7
0 +___ 5
3 8

a.

d.

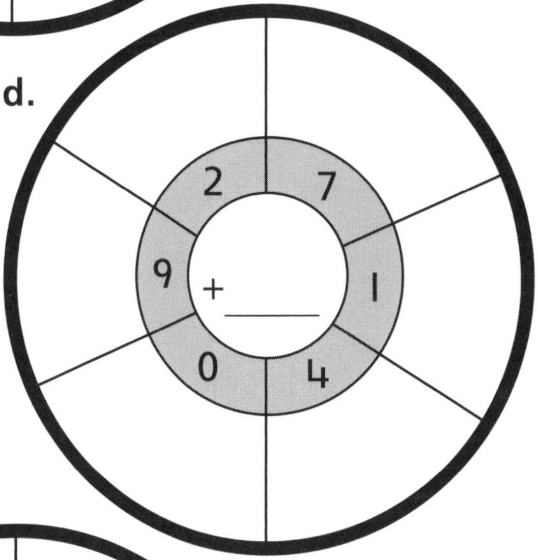

2 7
9 +___ 1
0 4

e.

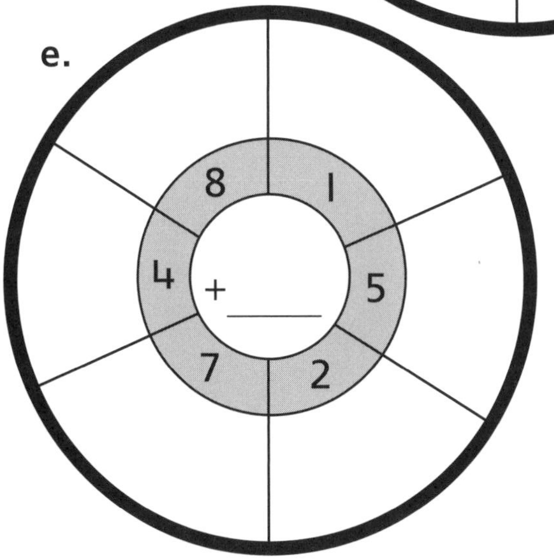

8 1
4 +___ 5
7 2

f.

8 9
3 +___ 6
7 5

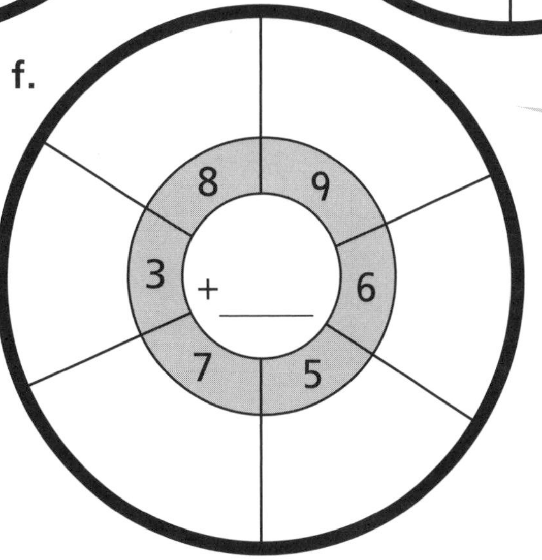

Number Board

1	2	3	4	5	6	7	8	9	10
11	12	13	14	15	16	17	18	19	20
21	22	23	24	25	26	27	28	29	30
31	32	33	34	35	36	37	38	39	40
41	42	43	44	45	46	47	48	49	50
51	52	53	54	55	56	57	58	59	60
61	62	63	64	65	66	67	68	69	70
71	72	73	74	75	76	77	78	79	80
81	82	83	84	85	86	87	88	89	90
91	92	93	94	95	96	97	98	99	100
101	102	103	104	105	106	107	108	109	110
111	112	113	114	115	116	117	118	119	120
121	122	123	124	125	126	127	128	129	130